TRIGONOMETRY

and the Elementary
Transcendental Functions

by **TOMLINSON FORT**
Professor of Mathematics
Emory University

THE MACMILLAN COMPANY, NEW YORK
COLLIER-MACMILLAN LIMITED, LONDON

Third Printing 1964

Library of Congress catalog card number: 63-9594

The Macmillan Company, New York
Collier-Macmillan Canada, Ltd., Toronto, Ontario
DIVISIONS OF THE CROWELL-COLLIER PUBLISHING COMPANY

Printed in the United States of America

A series of undergraduate mathematics texts under the editorship of Carl B. Allendoerfer

Preface

This book contains all the material of the conventional trigonometry course with, however, unusual attention given to fundamental concepts. In addition to this conventional material there is a careful study of the trigonometric functions and of the exponential and logarithm based on infinite power series definitions. Long experience both with pure and applied mathematics has convinced the author that there is no substitute for a sound knowledge of the elementary functions. Also in the opinion of the author this is most easily achieved by means of infinite series. The concepts of the limit of a sequence and hence of convergent and divergent series are as easily taught in the freshman year in college or in the senior year in high school as in the later years in college. A person must have patience to teach new ideas at any time.

If a teacher wishes to omit the part of the book depending upon series he can do so without in any way interrupting his work. He will find in addition to the usual applications a short chapter on the circular functions without introducing series and certain applications in physics. These he also can omit if he likes. Finally there is a chapter on complex numbers.

The oblique triangle is treated in detail but is put late in the book, in as much as the author regards other things as more important. However, the oblique triangle does pose many fine problems and it is a pity to omit it completely.

The content of the freshman course is a matter of endless difference of opinion. However, the author believes that many of the topics currently being introduced into the freshman year can be postponed and that the material in this book will give a sound basis for further work either for the mathematics major or for majors in science or engineering. As a terminal course for the general student it should serve its purpose better than most courses designed for this end.

T. F.

Atlanta, Georgia

EXAMINATION COPIES FOR COLLEGE
TEXTBOOK ADOPTION   DATE 6/3/66

CLINTON COMMUNITY COLLEGE

TITLE ____TRIGONOMETRY and the Elementary____

Transcendental
Functions____ AUTHOR _____by Tomlinson Fort__

C DATE __1963__ LATEST REVISION _____

PUBLISHER ___Macmillan_____

ADDRESS _____

List
__Hard____, COVER, Hard or paper $____--Price

This copy was obtained as an examination book, looking forward to adoption of a new text for:

_____MR. MOGCK_____

SUBJECT FOR TEXT CHANGE ___Trigonommetry___

Book publishing companies expect a statement from
the college as to the manner in which a book meets
our college textbook needs. Some publishing companies request the return of the examination copy in
(90 days) if not adopted as a text. By keeping this
sheet attached until the final decision, a loss of
contact can be avoided.

STATEMENT (Brief) as to how this text fits the
needs for the subject you teach. _____

_____

_____

NOTE: The above can be used to report to the publisher. Also, you are to file a TEXTBOOK EVALU-
ATION sheet for each book seriously considered for
adoption. These forms are available at the college
office.

Contents

Chapter 1

Numbers and Measurement

1. Numbers

The student undoubtedly has observed that most of his mathematics has been concerned with numbers. He has been working with what we shall call the *ordinary number system*. This is a part of his language. It has been developed over the ages by man for use in many problems. In this respect it differs not one whit from the rest of our language. The number system has had as its purpose the solving of problems where precision is required. As a consequence it is precise in a way that most language is not.

The number system was developed and used long before it was logically analyzed, just as the English language in general was developed and spoken before there was any formal study of grammar. There is little doubt that the earliest need for numbers was as a means of counting. As a consequence the positive rational integers, or, simply, the positive integers, may be thought of as a beginning point in the history of numbers. From this beginning the number system has been increased in response to the needs of an ever more complex civilization. A systematic logical study of numbers is something that every mathematician must make. However, to do this carefully would take far more time than can be allotted to such a study in this course. We shall be concerned primarily with the real numbers. To the mathematician the real numbers are just a set of objects he uses in his business.

As we all know the real numbers can be divided into subsets:

I. (a) the positive numbers
   (b) the negative numbers
   (c) zero.

It is possible to divide them into subsets in many other ways; for example,

II. (a) rational numbers
    (b) irrational numbers.

It may be a good idea to say what these terms mean.

DEFINITION: *A* **rational real** *number is a number that can be written in the form p/q where p and q are integers. An irrational number is one that can not be so written.*

We note that zero is an integer.

It is not evident that there are any irrational numbers. To open a discussion of this we prove a theorem that dates from ancient Greece and that has influenced the development of mathematics over the years as much as any other theorem.

THEOREM: *There is no rational number which when squared yields 2.*

Proof: Assume (a) that p and q are integers that have no common integral factor other than 1. Assume (b) that

$$(p/q)^2 = 2. \tag{1}$$

Now from (1)

$$p^2 = 2q^2. \tag{2}$$

Hence p^2 is even and consequently p is even. The student can convince himself readily that the square of every odd number is odd. Thus, the odd numbers, when written in the ordinary way, all end in 1, 3, 5, 7, or 9, and any number so ending is odd. Square any such number and the result ends in 1, 5, or 9, and consequently is odd. Similarly, the square of any even number is even. Now since p is even, we can let $p = 2k$ where k is an integer. From (2) we have

$$4k^2 = 2q^2,$$
$$2k^2 = q^2.$$

Consequently q^2 is even. Hence q is even. In other words, p and q both have the factor 2. This contradicts assumption (a) made above, and the theorem is proved.

What do mathematicians do about this situation? They define (make) a new positive number which they denote by $\sqrt{2}$. This number is such that

$$(\sqrt{2})^2 = 2.$$

People made the other numbers too. We know that $\sqrt{2}$ is irrational since we have just proved that it can not be rational. The student knows that another notation for $\sqrt{2}$ is $2^{1/2}$. This notation has many advantages over $\sqrt{2}$. There are numerous other irrational numbers. It is not difficult to prove that it is impossible to count them. The rational and irrational numbers have been studied extensively. They have interesting properties, many of which are undoubtedly familiar to the reader. One of the properties that will be of particular interest to us is that every irrational number can be approximated to any desired degree of accuracy by a rational number. Thus

$$1.4135 < \sqrt{2} < 1.4145.$$

Here, 1.4135 and 1.4145 are rational numbers. If this approximation is not sufficiently accurate for our purposes, we have a rule for calculating additional digits. We find, for example,

$$1.4142135 < \sqrt{2} < 1.4142145$$

and so on, to the number of decimal places desired. Of course, actually obtaining an approximation may be beyond our ability, but what of that?

EXERCISES

1. If a rule for the decimal approximation of a number leads to an unending succession of digits, does this mean that the number is irrational? Illustrate your answer with an example.

2. Prove that between any two rational numbers there is a third rational number and hence more than a million, more than a billion, etc.

3. Prove that there is no rational number which when cubed will yield 2.

4. A prime number is a positive integer which can be divided without a remainder by no integer except itself and 1. A theorem of great importance states that every positive integer can be factored into prime number factors in one and only one way. This is sometimes called the **fundamental theorem** of arithmetic. Its proof is beyond the scope of this book. For example,

$$280 = 2 \cdot 2 \cdot 2 \cdot 5 \cdot 7$$

cannot be factored into prime factors in any other way. Of course, we are not counting 1 as a factor.

Prove that there is no rational number which when squared will give a positive integer A if when A is factored into its prime factors some prime factor occurs an odd number of times.

5. Generalize the theorem of exercise 4 and prove your generalization.

6. Use the results of exercises 4 and 5 to define some irrational numbers.

2. Measurement of Line Segments

(a)   As the engineer does it

Let us consider two points marked by pins. The surveyor has a steel tape with lines drawn across it marking feet and tenths of a foot. He carefully stretches his tape in a way quite familiar to everyone and announces the length of the line segment between the two points in feet and tenths of a foot. If he is an engineer in a laboratory, he can read length to thousandths of an inch. He even may get schemes for much more refined measurement than this. We now point out to him that if he views a "line" on his tape or ruler under a microscope it looks quite wide and irregular. We even suggest that he view his "lines" and "points" under a supermicroscope showing the molecules of the material. They would be in rapid motion. We now ask him what he means by the "length of a line segment" anyhow. The mathematician requires a precise answer to this question. The engineer finds that he is lost in a haze and is unable to give a satisfactory definition based on engineering procedure.

(b)   As the physicist sees it

The physicist recognizes the inherent difficulty of the problem, but to him length is something to be studied and defined following that study. His definition is essentially a method of determination. The physicist is not in the least disturbed if later studies lead to another method of determination and consequently another definition.

(c)   As the mathematician sees it

The mathematician's line segment, of course, had its beginning in the pictures and other things used by the engineer. However, as viewed now his line segment is simply a segment (interval) of the real numbers. For convenience it is described in geometric language. However, the student must remember that the line segment of mathematics is not a thing of the drawing board. We shall, however, use the line segment of mathematics to study the line segment of the drawing board. Human experience over the ages justifies this procedure. We also use the line segment of the drawing board to suggest likely properties of the line segment of mathematics.

DEFINITION: *An* **open interval** *is the set of all real numbers x, such that*

$$a < x < b,$$

where a and b are particular numbers.

This interval frequently is denoted simply by (a, b).

DEFINITION: *A* **closed interval** *is the set of all real numbers x, such that*

$$a \leqq x \leqq b.$$

This interval is frequently denoted by $[a, b]$.

An interval may be closed at one end and open at the other; thus, $[a, b)$ or $(a, b]$.

3. The Linear Scale

Given a straight line as indicated in Fig. 1 we choose a point on this line and mark it 0. We call this the *origin*. We now choose a second point on this line which we designate as 1. We apply the line segment 0 to 1 along the line to get the points 2, 3, 4, · · ·; then we get the rational fractional points. This is an engineering process

The mathematician's line contains all these points and the irrational points too.

FIGURE 1

DEFINITION: *In mathematics the* **length** *of the interval from a to b (length of line segment) is the absolute[1] value of b − a.*

This is quite regardless of whether the interval is open or closed.

4. Direction

It is convenient in many places to have directed line segments. We shall see more of this later. We choose one direction (sense) on a line as positive and the opposite direction (sense) as negative. If we have a scaled line with 0 as origin, we speak of the distance from L_1, a point on the line, to a second point L_2 also on the line.

DEFINITION: *The* **distance** *from L_1 to L_2 is $L_2 − L_1$.*

We note that this distance from L_1 to L_2 is the negative of the distance from L_2 to L_1. *The length of the line segment L_1L_2 is the absolute value of the distance from L_1 to L_2.*

When there is no direction on a line segment the designations "distance from L_1 to L_2" and "length of the line segment from L_1 to L_2" will be interchangeable; both are positive.

5. The Cartesian Plane[2]

The student is undoubtedly familiar with x- and y-axes and the resulting coordinate system for points in a plane. Consequently, only the briefest description is given here. We remind the reader that he is dealing with the mathematician's number system and

---

[1]Denote the absolute value of a by $|a|$. If a is positive, $|a| = a$. If $a = 0$, $|a| = a$. If a is negative, $|a| = -a$. Thus $|2| = 2$, $|-2| = -(-2) = 2$.

[2]Named for René Descartes, a Latinized form of whose name was *Cartesius*.

only secondarily with the engineer's picture.

We assume *x*- and *y*-axes at right angles, each being a scaled line with common origin the point of intersection. The *x*-axis usually is drawn horizontal with positive direction to the right, the *y*-axis, vertical with positive direction upward. A point has as **coordinates** its distance from the axes, each measured parallel to the other axis and with its sign determined by that axis. Distances from the *y*-axis parallel to the *x*-axis are called **abscissas.** They are positive when measured to the right, negative when measured to the left. Distances from the *x*-axis parallel to the *y*-axis are called **ordinates.** They are positive when measured upward, negative when measured down-ward. The abscissa and ordinate are the coordinates of the point. We write (x, y) where x is the abscissa of the point and y is the or-dinate. The axes divide the plane into four quadrants numbered as indicated in Fig. 2. Points on an axis do not lie in any quadrant.

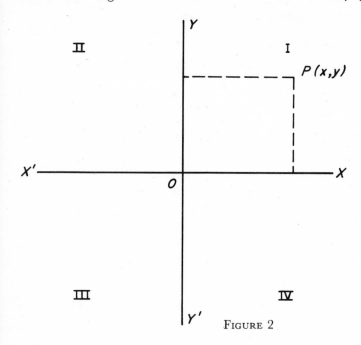

FIGURE 2

EXERCISES

1. Discuss the meaning of "length of a line segment."

2.   Discuss the meaning of "distance from L_1 to L_2."

3.   In which quadrant does a point lie if its abscissa is positive and its ordinate negative; if its abscissa is negative and ordinate positive; if both are negative?

4.   Draw a set of axes and mark the following points: (1, 1), (2, 0), (7, −8), (−13, 14), (0, 10), (0, 0), (−7, −6).

5.   Where can a point be if its abscissa equals its ordinate?

6.   Where can a point be if its ordinate is twice its abscissa?

7.   Where can a point be if its abscissa is 2? Where can a point be if its ordinate is 4?

8.   Draw the quadrilateral whose vertices are (−4, −1), (3, −1), (3, 2), (−4, 2). Prove that this quadrilateral is a rectangle.

9.   Find the coordinates of the point midway between the origin and the point (8, 10).

10.   The origin is midpoint of a line segment. One end of the segment is at the point (4, −6). What are the coordinates of the other end?

11.   Compute the distance from (3, 2) to (6, 6). This distance is undirected. (*Hint: Draw a figure and use the right triangle law $c^2 = a^2 + b^2$.*)

12.   Plot the points (7, 8), (6, −2). Compute the length of the line segment joining them.

13.   What is the distance from (0, 7) to (0, 10); from (0, 10) to (0, 7)?

14.   The midpoint of the horizontal base of an equilateral triangle is the origin. The length of each side is 10. What are the coordinates of the vertices?

15.   One vertex of a square is at (7, −11). Its sides are parallel to the axes and of length 10. Give all possible positions for other vertices.

Chapter 2

Functions

1. Sets

The concept of oneness is fundamental in mathematics and has been freely assumed in what has gone before in this book. The same thing has been done for the equally fundamental and closely related concept of a set. These concepts are among the earliest notions acquired in childhood and we can not begin mathematics without them.

2. Variable

DEFINITION: *A symbol such as a letter which stands for any element of a set is called a* **variable.**

The sets with which we are to deal are usually numbers and a variable will be a letter representing any unspecified member of a set of numbers. The term "variable" thus is a kind of misnomer. There is no movement or change. In applied mathematics, however, we do deal with things like time which change and to which the word "variable" can be applied with the ordinary understanding of what that term means.

DEFINITION: *A set of numbers may contain but one number. Under this circumstance the variable of the set is called a* **constant.**

The value of a constant may or may not be known. Calling something that has only one value a variable may seem like a contradiction but we must remember that with us the word "variable" is a technical term and has the meaning which we have given it. Frequently we do not know if the set of a variable consists of just one or more than one element or even of any element. It would be very inconvenient if we could not use one term to cover all cases, any one of which might prove to be the fact in a particular problem.

DEFINITION: *If we have a variable as x we shall speak of* **permissible values** *for x meaning those numbers of the set symbolized by x.*

Now in mathematics variables are usually connected with other variables in some way. We mean by this the following:

DEFINITION: *If in some way we are assured that if a variable is given one of its permissible values then a second variable is limited to certain of its permissible values we say that we have a* **correspondence.** *The values of the second variable just discussed are said to correspond to the value of the first.*

The most interesting kind of correspondence gives a function which we now proceed to define.

DEFINITION: *If to every permissible value of x there corresponds one and only one value of a second variable y and if every permissible value for y corresponds to some x then the set of ordered pairs (x, y) is called a* **function.** This is a definition. There is nothing to prove.

The permissible values for x are commonly called the *domain* of the function and the permissible values for y are then called the *range* of the function.

It is also customary to refer to x as the *independent variable* and y as the *dependent variable*. As a matter of fact it has been a long-established custom to say that: y is *a function of* x. We shall not hesitate to do this if it seems in the interest of clarity or brevity to do so. However, the student must remember that according to the definition just given the term *function* does not apply to y alone. There are two variables, the independent variable and the dependent variable.

3. *Examples of Functions*

(a)   *Functions defined by algebra*
A very important class of functions consists of those functions where the value of the dependent variable can be calculated by the rules of algebra (arithmetic) when a permissible value is given to the independent variable. Thus if $y = x^2$, where x is the independent variable and y the dependent variable, we have a function. The domain for x may be all numbers or any portion of the numbers required by the problem. The range is determined by the domain and the rules of arithmetic. Similarly $y = x^3 - x^2 - x - 1$ defines a function. *We shall in the earlier chapters of this book deal only with real numbers.* Under this agreement permissible numbers will always be real. Thus $y = \sqrt{x^3 - x^2 - x - 1}$ defines a function but the domain cannot include numbers which make $x^3 - x^2 - x - 1$ negative.

DEFINITION: *If a function can be defined by a formula involving the independent variable only and using no symbol of operation other than those of addition, subtraction, multiplication, division and the extraction of roots, then the function is called a* **simple algebraic function.**
Simple algebraic functions are further classified for convenience as indicated by the following definitions:

DEFINITION: *An expression,* $a_0 x^n + a_1 x^{n-1} + \cdot \cdot \cdot + a_n$ *where* $a_0, \cdot \cdot \cdot, a_n$ *are any numbers and where n is a positive integer or zero defines an* **integral rational function.** *The expression itself is frequently called a* **polynomial.**

DEFINITION: *A formula in x involving only the operations of addition, subtraction, multiplication, and division as applied to x defines a* **rational function** *of x.*

For example, $x^2 - 2x + 1$, $\dfrac{x - 1}{x + 1}$, $\dfrac{x^2 + 4x - \sqrt{3}}{\sqrt{2x} - 1}$ define rational functions in spite of the occurrence of $\sqrt{3}$ and $\sqrt{2}$. On the other hand, $\sqrt{x^2 + 1}$ defines an irrational simple algebraic function.

DEFINITION: *Any simple algebraic function that is not rational is called* **irrational.**

(b) Functions defined by geometry

The circumference of a circle is a function of the length of the radius. This is an example of a function defined by geometry. Notice the wording "is a function of." We have commented on this usage. It is convenient here.

(c) Functions in physics

The distance fallen by an object dropped from the top of a tower is a function of the time of falling. This is an example from physics.

An important problem in the study of functions defined by geometry, physics or other branches of endeavor is to work out a rule for calculating the value of the dependent variable when a permissible value is given to the independent variable. We desire a rule that involves only recognized mathematical procedures.

4. Function Notation

Frequently, for convenience, when we have a function involving two variables as x and y we write

$$y = f(x).$$

This is read "y is a function of x" or more usually "y equals f of x." A more precise reading would be "$y = f(x)$ defines a function." The letter f is frequently replaced by other letters as $y = F(x)$, $y = \phi(x)$, or $y = G(x)$. These can be read "y equals cap f of x," "y equals phi of x", etc.

EXERCISES

1. Give definitions of: **(a)** variable; **(b)** function; **(c)** independent variable; **(d)** dependent variable.

2. A function is defined by each of the following equations. Tell which are rational, irrational, integral rational. Assuming that we are restricted to real numbers only and not otherwise restricted, state permissible values for x in each case.

(a) $y = x^2 + 2x - 1$. (b) $y = \dfrac{x^2 + 1}{x^2 - 1}$. (c) $y = \sqrt{x^2 + 3x - 1}$.

(d) $y = \sqrt[3]{x^2 + 3x} - 1$. (e) $y = \sqrt{x^2 - 2x} + 1$. (f) $y = \sqrt{x} + \sqrt{x + 1}$.

(g) $y = \sqrt[3]{x + 1}$. (h) $\dfrac{1}{y + 2} = \sqrt{x + 1}$.

3. Given $y = f(x)$ find $f(1), f(2), f(3), f(2a + 1), f(2x + 1)$ and $f\left(\dfrac{1}{2x + 1}\right)$, where

(a) $f(x) = \dfrac{x + 1}{x - 4}$; (b) $f(x) = x^3 - 3x^2 + 2x - 1$; (c) $f(x) = \sqrt{x^2 + 1}$.

4. Give four functions defined by geometry.
5. Give four functions defined by physics.
6. Give four functions defined by business.

5. On Division by Zero and on Becoming Infinite

In arithmetic to divide a number b by a number c means to find all numbers which when multiplied by c yield b. Now to divide 1 by 0 would mean to find those numbers which when multiplied by 0 yield 1. The student knows that there is no such number because every number when multiplied by 0 yields 0. Similarly, to divide 0 by 0 would mean to find those numbers which when multiplied by 0 yield 0. Any number whatever fulfills this requirement. This is not a useful answer. Consequently, mathematicians do not define division by 0 under any circumstances. The student frequently will hear or read the statement "Division by zero is not defined."

There is no largest number. If you should work hard for ten years to write the largest number, someone could come along and annex a zero and thus in one second have a number ten times as big as the one you had worked so hard to write. However, consider the function defined by $y = 1/x^2$. The value 0 is not permissible. However, if x is numerically less than $1/10$ then y is greater than 100. If x is numerically less than $1/1000$ then y is greater than 1,000,000. Mention any positive number M, no matter how great, then y will be greater than M if $|x| < 1/\sqrt{M}$. It is customary to say that y **becomes infinite** when x approaches 0. The statement "y approaches infinity" is to be avoided for it implies that there is a number called infinity. It is particularly to be noticed that although we have said "x approaches 0" there is no motion. We only make choices for x and discuss the corresponding values for y.

The expressions "become positively infinite" and "become negatively infinite" may be used in case all values of y are positive or in case all values of y are negative when x is sufficiently close to a. We may have mixed situations, for example $y > 0$ when $x > a$ and $y < 0$ when $x > a$.

Example 1: $y = 1/x^2$. Here y becomes positively infinite at $x = 0$.

Example 2: $y = 1/x$. Here y becomes infinite at $x = 0$ but $y > 0$ if $x > 0$ and $y < 0$ if $x < 0$.

EXERCISES

1. Describe the behavior of y in the neighborhood of $x = 0$ where:

(a) $y = \dfrac{1}{x^4}$;   (b) $y = \dfrac{1}{x^3}$;   (c) $y = \dfrac{1}{x^{2/3}}$;   (d) $y = \dfrac{1}{x^{3/2}}$.

2. Describe the behavior of y in the neighborhood of:

(a) $x = 2$; (b) $x = -3$; (c) $x = 3$, where $y = \dfrac{1}{(x-2)(x+3)(x-3)^2}$.

3. Describe the behavior of the following functions in the neighborhood of the point indicated. The letter y is omitted.
(a) $x + 1/x$, $x = 0$.   (b) $1/x^3 + 1/x^2$, $x = 0$.   (c) $1/x + 1/\sqrt{x}$, $x = 0$.
(d) $1/(x-2)^5 + 1/(x-2)^4 + 1/(x-2)^3$, $x = 2$.
(e) $(x^2+1)/(x^2-1)$, $x = 1$.   (f) x^2/x^3, $x = 0$.   (g) x^3/x^2, $x = 0$.

6. The Graph of a Function

The student has undoubtedly already drawn graphs. If we are given a function we can let the independent variable be pictured as an abscissa and the corresponding value of the dependent variable as an ordinate. We thus have a point in the plane for every permissible value of the independent variable. The totality of such points constitutes the graph of the function. If the function is defined by an equation this same figure may be referred to as the **locus,** or **graph,** of the equation.

Graphs may be interesting in themselves and the function may be a tool for studying them. On the other hand, this is a two-way affair, and the graph frequently is a very powerful tool for the study of the function. It is this last use with which we shall be primarily concerned in this course.

Example 1: The graph of $y = 2x + 4$ is a straight line as indicated in Fig. 3.

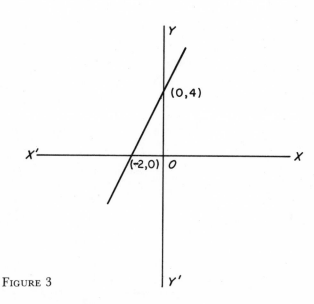

FIGURE 3

Example 2:   The graph of $y = |x|$ is composed of two half-lines as indicated in Fig. 4.

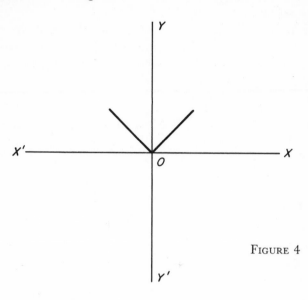

FIGURE 4

Example 3:   The graph of $y = x^2 - 5x + 6$ is as indicated in Fig. 5.

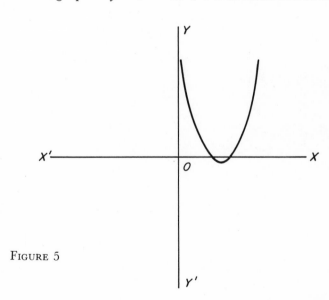

FIGURE 5

Example 4.   The graph of $y = |x^2 - 5x + 6|$ is as indicated in Fig. 6.

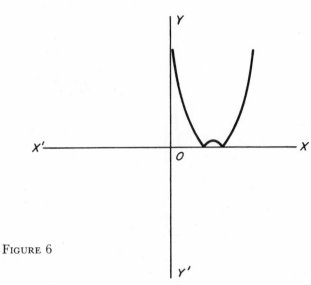

FIGURE 6

Example 5.   The graph of $y = 1/x$ is as indicated in Fig. 7. This graph has an interesting relation to the y-axis which is referred to as an *asymptote* of the graph.

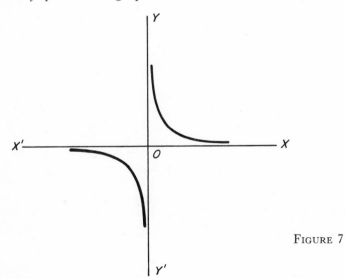

FIGURE 7

Example 6:   The graph of $y = 1/(x - 1)^2$ is as indicated in Fig. 8. The line parallel to the y-axis and one unit to the right is an asymptote to the graph.

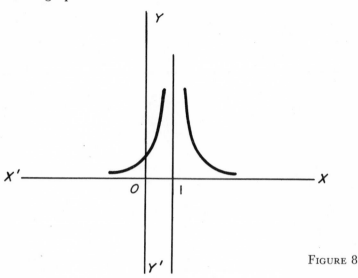

FIGURE 8

EXERCISES

1.   Construct graphs for the functions defined by the following equations:

(a) $y = 7x - 2$;
(b) $y = -3x + 1$;
(c) $y = -x^2 + 2x + 1$;
(d) $y = |-x^2 + 2x + 1|$;
(e) $y = |-x^2 + 2x + 10|$;
(f) $y = x^3$;
(g) $y = x + 1/x - 1$;
(h) $y = 1/(x + 1)(x - 1)(x + 2)$;
(i) $y = \sqrt{x}$;
(j) $y = |x^3|$;
(k) $y = (x - 1)(x - 2)(x - 3)$;
(l) $y = x$ when $0 \leq x < 1$,
(m) $y = 1$, $0 \leq x < 1$;
      $y = 2x$ when $1 \leq x < 2$,
      $y = 2$, $1 \leq x < 2$.
      $y = 3x$ when $2 \leq x \leq 3$;

2.   The gravitational attraction of the earth on a particle outside the earth varies inversely as the square of its distance from the center of the earth. If the particle is inside the earth the gravitational attraction varies directly as its distance from the center of the earth. Express these facts by means of equations. Draw a graph.

Chapter 3

Angles

1. Rays

DEFINITION: *A directed straight line with given beginning point, direction, and sense, but with unbounded length, is called a ray.*

A ray is frequently described as a directed *half-line*.

A ray has an **origin** that is a beginning point but has no end. A line segment of any length, no matter how great, can be placed along the ray with one end at the origin of the ray and still the ray will extend beyond the other end of the line segment. This fact is frequently described by saying that the ray is *infinite in length*. Of course it is not possible to draw a picture representing all of a ray on your paper, any more than it is possible to draw a picture representing all of a straight line. A ray is usually represented by a straight line segment with marked origin and sense (see Fig. 9). Notice that no end point is marked.

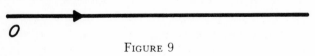

O

FIGURE 9

19

2. Point Sets

We present for review a few facts about point sets which may be familiar to the student.

DEFINITION: *The points common to two point sets A and B constitute a set called the intersection of A and B.*

We may still use the word *intersection*, even if A and B have no point in common. In this case the intersection clearly contains no point. For some purposes this is a more convenient terminology than simply saying that the sets do not intersect.

DEFINITION: *All those points which lie in either A or B or both constitute a point set called the union of A and B.*

DEFINITION: *A point set B is called a subset of A if all the points of B are also points of A.*

DEFINITION: *Given a set of points A and a subset of A which we call B, then those points of A which are not in B are called the* **complement** *of B with respect to A.*

In the event that A and B are identical we may still speak of the complement of B with respect to A. Of course, this complement contains no point.

3. Definition of Angle

Consider the union of two rays with common origin. We give without proof the following theorem. It probably will not be challenged by the student. However a careful proof is none too easy.

THEOREM: *The union of two noncoincident rays with the same origin divides the plane into two distinct regions.*

Each region contains points.

No point in one region is also in the other.

Each point of the plane with the exception of the points of the rays lies in one or the other of the two regions.

By agreement the points of the rays lie in neither region.

The union of the two rays is called the **boundary** of each of the regions.

Two points are in the same region if the straight line segment joining them either does not intersect the boundary of the region or intersects this boundary exactly twice. Two points are in different regions if the straight line segment joining them intersects the common boundary of the two regions exactly once (see Figs. 10a and 10b). A line passing through the common origin as in Fig. 10c is defined to intersect the boundary exactly twice.

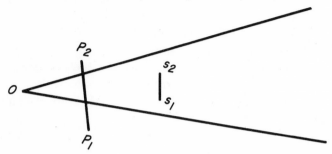

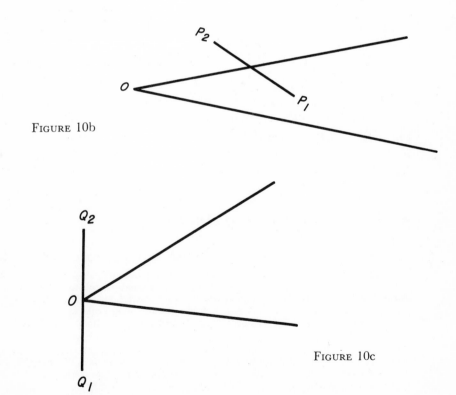

FIGURE 10a

FIGURE 10b

FIGURE 10c

DEFINITION: *Each of the regions, as just described, into which the plane is divided by two noncoincident rays with common origin is called an* **angle.**[1]

The rays are called the **sides** *of the angle and the common origin of the rays is called the* **vertex** *of the angle.*

If the student likes he may say that an angle is a portion of a plane bounded by two rays with common origin.

We shall call the plane from which the two rays with common origin have been removed the **deleted plane.** We then say that each of the two angles into which the plane is divided is the complement of the other with reference to the deleted plane.[2]

If the two rays forming the boundary of an angle lie in the same straight line, but with different senses, the angle is called a **straight angle.**

If two rays with common origin lie in the same straight line and have the same sense, they are said to form a **zero angle.** The student may say that there is only one ray. This is strictly true. Yet the fiction of coincident but different rays is a very useful one.

Two angles that can be superposed the one upon the other are called **congruent.**

If a straight angle is divided by a third ray into two congruent angles, each of the angles into which it is divided is called a **right angle.**

DEFINITION: *The angles formed by two intersecting directed line segments are the angles formed by two rays with common origin, the point of intersection of the line segments, and the respective directions and senses of the line segments.*

4. The Measurement of Angles

When talking of a line segment we have two concepts: (1) the

[1]Other definitions of an angle are possible. See, for example, *Projective Geometry* by Veblen and Young, where an angle is defined as an ordered pair of rays with common origin (Vol. II, p. 59). The definition which we give makes an angle a region in the plane. This lends itself readily to a definition of "measure of an angle."

For an axiomatic study of angle see Hans Zassenhaus, *Amer. Math. Monthly*, Vol. 61 (1954), p. 369.

[2]The term "complement" is most frequently used when each of two angles is the complement of the other with reference to a right angle. So general is this practice that we usually just say "complementary angles" not mentioning a right angle.

picture and the idealized mathematician's counterpart, and (2) the measure of its extent, to which the name "length" is given.

Now when we come to angles we have likewise: (a) the picture and idealized counterpart and (b) the measure of extent which we are now to discuss. Unfortunately, there is no commonly accepted name for the measure of the extent of an angle like "length" of a line segment. The term "angle" is indiscriminately used for (a) the geometric object and (b) the measure of the extent of that object. This has caused untold confusion. We can suggest names, but it seems hopeless to get any name generally accepted and used. We shall speak of the *measure of the angle or sometimes simply of the angle, meaning the same thing*. We may sometimes speak of the size of the angle. It is hoped that there will never be any ambiguity.

(a)   *As an engineer might see it*
The measurement of angles is accomplished in much the same way that straight line segments are measured. A certain angle is taken as a unit and applied to the given angle. The measure of the angle is read in terms of this unit.

(b)   *As the mathematician might see it*
Length is a measure of the extent of a line segment. The mathematician desires a similar measure for the extent of an angle. Before defining this, however, he defines a measure for the length of a circular arc. Take the circular arc and inscribe in it a broken line as indicated in Fig. 11. The length of this broken line is the sum of

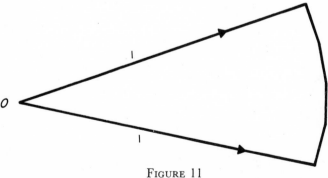

FIGURE 11

the lengths of the line segments of which it is composed. Now it will be proved in the student's calculus course that when the number of segments is increased indefinitely, each segment approaching zero in

length, then the length of the whole broken line has a limit which
we call the length of the circular arc. A careful analysis of the notion
of a limit will also be made in the calculus course. The important
thing now is to realize that a circular arc has measure in terms of a
linear unit. This measure is not something that is discovered. It is
something that is defined. The term "length of a circular arc" has
no meaning till we give it a meaning.

DEFINITION: *Given an angle, a circle of unit radius is drawn about
the vertex of the angle as center and lying in the plane of the angle as illustrated
in Fig. 12.   The length of the circular arc subtending the angle is a* **measure
of the angle.**[3]

The word subtend is best explained by a figure. In Fig. 12 the
angle α is subtended by the arc AB.

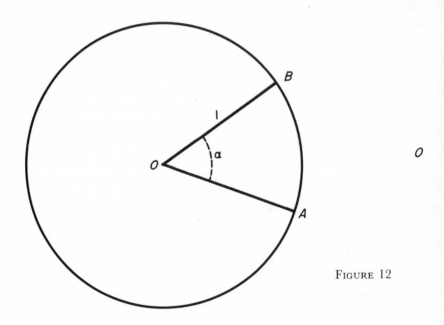

O

FIGURE 12

It is customary to give the measure of an angle in units to which
a name is given.

DEFINITION: *The angle with vertex at the center of a circle of radius 1
subtended by an arc of length 1 is called a* **radian.**

[3]In many ways a more natural measure would be the area of the circular sector. However, this is contrary to standard procedure.

An arc of a circle of radius 1 which is s_1 units in length subtends an angle of s_1 radians

Now the length of a circular arc of fixed central angle is proportional to the radius of the circle.

$$\frac{\text{length of arc}}{\text{length of radius}} = \text{constant}$$

With this assumption, we have the following theorem:

THEOREM: *Let θ be the measure of an angle as defined above. If the angle is at the center of a circle with radius of length r and if s is the length of the intercepted arc then*

$$s = r\,\theta \tag{1}$$

where θ is measured in radians.

Proof: Let s_1 be the length of the arc of a circle of radius 1 intercepted by the sides of the angle, then

$$\frac{s}{r} = \frac{s_1}{1} = \theta$$

Hence $s = r\,\theta$.

Formula (1) is basic in many things having to do with angles.

5. *Rotations and Large Angles*

There is no motion in the definition which we have given of an angle. This is the case in geometry. Now much of trigonometry is concerned with the measurement of triangles as we shall see. This is merely a geometric problem. There is no motion involved and all angles have measures less than the measure of a straight angle.

If we introduce motion into geometry we have what is no longer known as geometry but is called **kinematics.** So many applications of trigonometry are in kinematics that we must change the notion of angle as necessary to treat these problems. We shall be particularly concerned with rotation. The word angle as used in this connection is the measure of an amount of rotation. In this connection when we speak of an angle $\pi/4$, we mean a rotation of $\pi/4$ radians. A ray moves, changing its direction by $\pi/4$ radians. Of course, rotations are not limited in amount. A wheel may revolve many times, and we consequently have angles of any magnitude. Thus 2π is the measure of (describes) one complete revolution. Similarly $9\pi/2$ measures two and one-quarter complete revolutions. There is nothing fundamental in the unit used. This will be made clear in the next section. The student should extend formula (1) to angles of any magnitude.

6. *Angular units*

The radian is not the only unit in common use for measuring angles. There are also the following:

(a)   *The straight angle.*

This is a natural unit and is sometimes used.

(b)   *The right angle.*

This is also a natural unit and is frequently used.

(c)   *The* **revolution**.

This is by definition two straight angles. In studying rotations the revolution is a natural unit.

(d)   *The degree.*

One-ninetieth of a right angle is called a **degree.** It is a unit that has been used for a long time. It is still widely used. There are subunits according to the following table:

$$1 \text{ degree} = 60 \text{ minutes or } 1° = 60';$$
$$1 \text{ minute} = 60 \text{ seconds or } 1' = 60''.$$

(e)   *The* **grad.**   Occasionally, the right angle is divided into one hundred parts. One of which is assumed as a unit. This unit is sometimes called a **grad.**

(f)   *The* **radian.**   An alternative method of defining a **radian** to that already discussed is the following:

A radian is an angle such that π radians equal a straight angle. Here $\pi = 3.1415927 \cdot \cdot \cdot$ is a number that occurs in many places in mathematics. It is irrational. The student has probably already

encountered π. A radian may be denoted by r, thus $\dfrac{\pi}{2}r$. However, when radian measure is used customarily no symbol is used. Thus "an angle of measure $\pi/2$" means $\pi/2$ radians. Let the student compare the previous discussion of radian measure with this definition.

(g) *The* **mil.** In many military problems a unit of $1/1600$ of a right angle, which is called a **mil,** is used. The mil is approximately $1/1000$ of a radian and it is to this fact that it owes its chief usefulness.

One mil is denoted by m.

The units of angular measure that we have discussed are connected by the following relations which give the measure of the unit of one system in terms of the unit of the second system. These relations permit us to find the measure of an angle in terms of any unit if its measure in terms of one of the other units is known.

TABLE 1

1 revolution = 2 straight angles
1 revolution = 4 right angles
1 revolution = 360 degrees
1 revolution = 2π radians
1 revolution = 6400 mils

TABLE 2

1 straight angle = $\frac{1}{2}$ revolution
1 straight angle = 2 right angles
1 straight angle = 180 degrees
1 straight angle = π radians
1 straight angle = 3200 mils

TABLE 3

1 right angle = $\frac{1}{4}$ revolution
1 right angle = $\frac{1}{2}$ straight angle
1 right angle = 90 degrees
1 right angle = $\frac{\pi}{2}$ radians

TABLE 4

1 degree = $\frac{1}{360}$ revolution
1 degree = $\frac{1}{180}$ straight angle
1 degree = $\frac{1}{90}$ right angle
1 degree = $\frac{\pi}{180}$ radians
1 degree = $\frac{160}{9}$ mils

TABLE 5

1 radian = $\frac{1}{2\pi}$ revolutions
1 radian = $\frac{1}{\pi}$ straight angles
1 radian = $\frac{2}{\pi}$ right angles
1 radian = $\frac{180}{\pi}$ degrees
1 radian = $\frac{3200}{\pi}$ mils

TABLE 6

1 mil = $\frac{1}{6400}$ revolution
1 mil = $\frac{1}{3200}$ straight angles
1 mil = $\frac{1}{1600}$ right angles
1 mil = $\frac{9}{160}$ degrees
1 mil = $\frac{\pi}{3200}$ radians

In measuring lengths the rod which is used is called a ruler. The corresponding instrument for measuring angles is called a **protractor.** Figure 13 shows a protractor with the degree as unit.

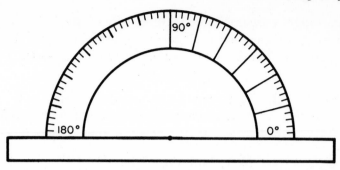

FIGURE 13

A protractor can be made with any unit. If, however, the only available protractor has the degree as unit, remember that we can readily reduce the measure of angle given in any of the units which we have discussed to degrees. If a measure is given in degrees, by means of these same tables it can be written in any of the other units.

No table was made for the grad. This unit is not often used.

7. *Notation*

The natural way to describe the angle formed by the rays OA and OB is simply to write (OA, OB). If we denote the rays by a and b we write (a, b). However, the student is so accustomed to reading the angle with vertex at B as angle ABC or angle CBA when studying triangles or other polygons, that we shall do it ourselves from time to time and can not object to his doing so.

Angles will frequently be denoted by a single Greek letter as α. Here α represents the angle or the measure of the angle as the context implies.

8. *Directed Angles*

Just as we have directed straight line segments so we can have directed angles. For many purposes this is a very convenient thing. Curved arrows indicate sense or direction (Fig. 14)

Here the ray a is frequently called the **initial ray** or *initial side* and the ray b the **terminal ray** or *terminal side*. We speak of the angle (a, b) in distinction from the angle (b, a).

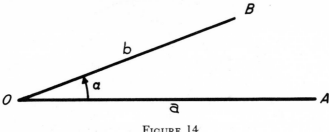

FIGURE 14

We also may read "the angle from *a* to *b*" or "the angle from *b* to *a*" as the case may be.

9. *Angles in Standard Position*

In the formal study of the measurement of angles it is customary to take the vertex of the angle at the origin of coordinates and the positive ray of the *x*-axis as *initial ray*, usually called *initial side*. The other ray of the angle is called the *terminal ray* or *terminal side*. The measurement is from the initial side to the terminal side. If the measurement is in a counterclockwise sense the angle is called *positive*. If it is in a clockwise sense the angle is called *negative*. This is just as simple as saying that distances measured along the *x*-axis to the right from the origin are positive and to the left negative. Clockwise direction means as the hands of a clock rotate and counterclockwise means in the opposite direction. The whole thing is clarified by Figs. 15 and 16 in which curved arrows again indicate the direction of measuring.

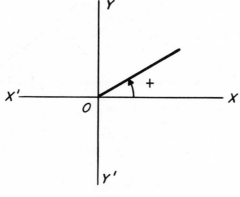

FIGURE 15

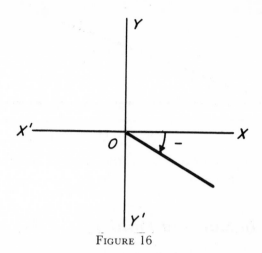

FIGURE 16

We note that the axes divide the plane into four quadrants. *An angle is said to be in that quadrant in which its terminal side lies. If the terminal side is on an axis the angle is called a quadrantal angle.*

10. Angles of a Triangle or other Polygon

Given a triangle as ABC, an angle of this triangle is the angle formed by two sides of the triangle considered as directed line segments from the vertex and including the region within the triangle. The same thing is true of any polygon.

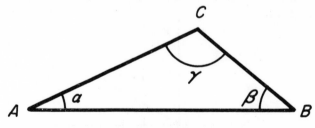

FIGURE 17

We speak of the angles α, β, γ or simply A, B, C. Sometimes these letters are used to describe the angle with letter at the vertex in the middle:

$$\alpha = BAC = CAB.$$

The angles of a polygon will be undirected unless the contrary is stated.

EXERCISES

1. Construct a set of X and Y axes and mark the points with the following co-ordinates: (1, 2), (3, 4), (7, 6), (−1, 2), (3, −4), (7, 6), (0, 10), (10, 0), (0, 0), (1, $\sqrt{2}$), ($\sqrt{2}$, $\sqrt{3}$), (−$\sqrt{2}$, −$\sqrt{3}$).

2. Find the radian measure of the angles whose measure in degrees is given: 30°, 45°, 120°, 180°, 2000°, −1500°, −2500°.

3. Find the corresponding degree measure of the angles whose radian measure is given: π, $\pi/2$, $\pi/4$, $\pi/3$, $\pi/6$, 1, 2, 3, −2½, −3.5, 7.8.

4. Find the corresponding measure in mils of the following angles whose measure in degrees is given: 3°, 2½°, 3° 24′ 13″, −12°, −0.001°, −(1° 13′ 24″).

5. Find the measure in degrees of the following angles whose measure in mils is given: 24m, 10m, 50m, −13m.

6. Find the measure in mils of the following angles whose measure in radians is given: 0.001, 0.01, 0.1, $\pi/90$, $\pi/360$, 1, 1.1, 1.01, 1.001.

7. Find the measure in radians of the following angles whose measure in mils is given: 1m, 10m, 8m, 7m, −4m, −2m, −15m.

8. Take a protractor and construct carefully the following angles:

    (1)   1 right angle, 4 right angles, 3½ right angles, −1 right angle, −4 right angles, −3½ right angles.

    (b)   30°, 120°, 255°, −30°, −100°, −255°.

    (c) π radians, $\pi/2$ radians, $\pi/6$ radians, −$\pi/6$ radians, −$\pi/2$ radians, −$\pi/3$ radians.

    (d)   800m, 400m, 3200m, −800m, −400m, −3200m.

9. If the minute hand of a watch is 0.5 inches long, what distance will the tip move in 15 minutes?

10. If the hour hand of a watch is 0.5 inches long, how far will its tip move in 30 days 10 hours and 20 minutes?

11. If the wheel of an automobile has a radius of 12 inches, how far will the auto-mobile go if there is no slipping and if the wheel rotates through an angle[4] of 125 radians; through an angle of 2175 degrees; of 7642 mills?

12. Prove: The area of a sector of a circle of radius r is $\frac{1}{2}r^2\theta$ where θ is the measure of the central angle in radians.

13. If a certain sheet metal costs 25¢ per square foot, find the cost of a piece of metal in the form of a sector of a circle of radius 5 feet and central angle 30°.

14. If the radius of a circle is 1000 feet and an arc is 1 foot long, what angle in mils is subtended at the center of the circle by the arc?

15. An officer on a ship sees another ship broadside which he knows to be 628 feet long. His instruments tell him that the ship subtends 10 mils at his eye. Approximately how far off is the ship?

    [4]Here the word *measure* is omitted before the 125, and in other places.

16. Suppose that an "object" is known to be 10 nautical miles away. It subtends at the eye of the observer an angle of 20 mils. Approximately how long is it in feet?

17. An object is known to be 10 nautical miles away. It subtends an angle of 1' at the eye of the observer. Approximately how long is it in yards?

18. Write a five-page essay on the measurement of line segments and of angles.

19. Write a five-page essay on angular units.

20. Write a five-page essay on linear units. Use an encyclopedia or other reference books.

The Trigonometric Functions

1. Triangles

Certain functions defined in terms of the measure of an angle and the measures of line segments are known as **trigonometric functions** and have proved to be of the greatest utility in mathematics. These functions get the name "trigonometric" from their use in the measurement of triangles, but they now have uses in a great many other places.

The study of the trigonometric functions and certain of their more elementary applications is a major purpose of this course. Before entering this study, however, we must review briefly a few facts about triangles. It is assumed that a study of these theorems and definitions already has been made by the student.

THEOREM I: *The sum of the measures of the three angles of any triangle is a straight angle.*

DEFINITION: *A triangle is called a* **right triangle** *if one of its angles is a right angle.*

DEFINITION: *Two angles are called equal if the measure of the one is equal to the measure of the other.*

DEFINITION: *A triangle is called* **isosceles** *if two of its sides are equal in length.*

DEFINITION: *A triangle is called* **equilateral** *if all three of its sides are equal in length.*

THEOREM II: *A triangle is isosceles if two of its angles are equal. Sides opposite equal angles are equal.*

THEOREM III: *If the angles of a triangle are all equal, the triangle is equilateral.*

DEFINITION: *If the angles of a triangle are respectively equal to the angles of a second triangle, then the triangles are called* **similar.** *Sides opposite equal angles are called* **homologous.**

THEOREM IV: *Two right triangles are similar if an acute angle of the one equals an acute angle of the other.*

THEOREM V: *All equilateral triangles are similar.*

THEOREM VI: *Given two similar triangles ABC and $A'B'C'$ where $<A = <A'$, $<B = <B'$, $<C = <C'$, let AB denote the length of the side joining A and B, etc.; then*

$$\frac{AB}{A'B'} = \frac{BC}{B'C'} = \frac{CA}{C'A'}.$$

This theorem can be briefly stated: *Homologous sides of similar triangles are proportional.*

2. Definition of the Functions

We review here what has been described already but with a slightly different point of view. In studying the trigonometric functions, it is convenient to use axes. However, let us realize that the axes are a tool. They may be placed where we like. The angle that we are studying is the fundamental thing.

We consider directed angles. Place the origin of coordinates at the vertex of the angle. Place the x-axis along the initial side. This is illustrated in Fig. 18. As the student well knows, the angles are designated positive if read in the counterclockwise sense and negative when read in the clockwise sense. The abscissa and ordinate of a point P are measured according to a scheme also well understood by the student. *We shall assume that*

$$r = \sqrt{x^2 + y^2}$$

is always positive.

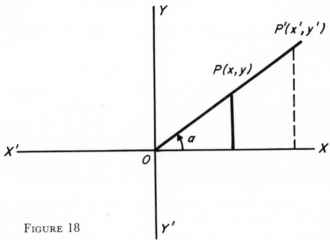

FIGURE 18

We remark that an angle is said to be in that quadrant in which its terminal side lies. If the terminal side lies on an axis, the angle is called a *quadrantal* angle. It does not lie in any quadrant.

THEOREM: *The ratios* $\dfrac{y}{r}, \dfrac{x}{r}, \dfrac{y}{x}, \dfrac{x}{y}, \dfrac{r}{x}$, *and* $\dfrac{r}{y}$, *where no denominator*

is zero, are independent of the location of P on the terminal side.

Proof: Choose two points P and P'. The triangles OMP and $OM'P'$ are similar since they are right triangles with one angle in common. If x is positive so is x', and if x' is positive so is x. The same is true of y and y'. We know that homologous sides of similar triangles are proportional. Hence we have the theorem.

We now define the functions. *Permissible angles* are angles for which the formula defining the functions determines a number.

The *domain of anyone of the functions consists of the measures of all permissible angles.* We refer to Fig. 18. Denote the measure of the angle by α. The point P is never taken at the origin.

$$\text{sine } \alpha = \frac{y}{r} \qquad\qquad \text{cosine } \alpha = \frac{x}{r}$$

$$\text{tangent } \alpha = \frac{y}{x}, \qquad x \neq 0 \qquad \text{cotangent } \alpha = \frac{x}{y}, \qquad y \neq 0$$

$$\text{secant } \alpha = \frac{r}{x}, \qquad x \neq 0 \qquad \text{cosecant } \alpha = \frac{r}{y}, \qquad y \neq 0$$

We usually abbreviate these and write

$$\sin \alpha = \frac{y}{r}, \qquad\qquad \cos \alpha = \frac{x}{r},$$

$$\tan \alpha = \frac{y}{x}, \qquad\qquad \cot \alpha = \frac{x}{y},$$

$$\sec \alpha = \frac{r}{x}, \qquad\qquad \csc \alpha = \frac{r}{y}.$$

Some people like to remember these definitions in words. Thus:

1. "The sine of an angle is equal to the ordinate over the distance."

2. "The tangent of an angle is equal to the ordinate over the abscissa."

Rules for determining the values of the trigonometric functions given a particular angle are highly desirable. If we did not have such rules much of the interest and utility of the trigonometric functions would be nonexistent. Rules for approximate calculation of the functions are well known and will be given later in this course. Unfortunately, were we to study these rules now so much time would be required for preliminary work that our attention would be deflected from the character of the functions themselves and from their elementary applications. Consequently, this highly important matter is postponed till Chapter 13. Right now we content ourselves with the knowledge that to every permissible angle there corresponds one and only one value of the function. Here, as frequently, the word "function" means **dependent variable.**

EXERCISES

1. Prove Theorem I.

2. Prove Theorem II.
3. Prove Theorem III.
4. We speak of the *measure* of an angle. Describe in detail what is meant.
5. Give in words definitions for all six trigonometric functions.
6. What are permissible angles for each of the six trigonometric functions?
7. Does 90° have a tangent? Does $\pi/2$ have a tangent?
8. For what values of α is $\sin \alpha = \cos \alpha$?
9. For what values of α is $\tan \alpha = \cot \alpha$?
10. Is it true that $\cos \alpha = \sin (90° - \alpha)$ for all values of α?
11. What is the difference between $\sin 45°$ and $\sin \pi/4$?
12. Prove: $\sin 45° = \sin 405°$.
13. Prove: $\cos \pi/6 = \cos (13\pi/6)$.
14. What are numerical values for $\sin 0$, $\sin \pi/2$, $\cos 3\pi/2$, $\tan \pi/4$, $\cot \pi/4$.
15. What are numerical values for $\sin 90°$, $\cos 180°$, $\tan 360°$, $\cot 270°$?
16. What are numerical values for $\sin 1600$ mils, $\cos 0$ mils, $\tan 3200$ mils?
17. Go to an encyclopedia and look up *Pythagoras* and give a report to the class on his life and works.
18. Go to an encyclopedia and look up Ptolemy and give a report to the class on his life and works.
19. Go to an encyclopedia and look up *Hipparchus* and give a report to the class on his life and works.
20. Consult any book that you wish to find the country and dates of the following men: *Descartes, Euler.*
21. A theorem which bears the modifier *Pythagorean* follows. Prove it.

Theorem: The area of a square constructed with the hypotenuse of a right triangle as a side is equal to the sum of the areas of the squares constructed, respectively, with the legs of the triangle as sides.

3. *Functions of Complementary Angles*

Draw a right triangle.

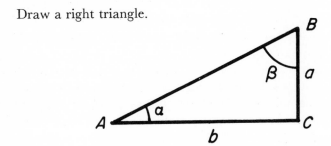

FIGURE 19

If the angle α is put in standard position

$$\frac{a}{r} = \sin \alpha.$$

If the angle β is put in standard position

$$\frac{a}{r} = \cos \beta.$$

Hence

$$\sin \alpha = \cos \beta. \tag{1}$$

But α and β are **complementary angles;** that is, $\alpha + \beta = $ a right angle. Relationship (1) holds for all angles either positive or negative whose sum is one right angle. This will be proved later. The ambitious student should see if he can prove it at this stage.

We express equation (1) by saying:

The sine of an angle is the cosine of its complement. Similarly,

1. *The secant of an angle is the cosecant of its complement if both are defined.*

2. *The tangent of an angle is the cotangent of its complement if both are defined.*

4. *Functions of 30°, 45°, 60°* $(\pi/6, \pi/4, \pi/3)$

It happens that we can find easily and by strictly elementary methods the trigonometric functions of 30°, 45°, and 60°. It also happens that in the applications of the trigonometric functions these angles are of frequent occurrence.

We draw two triangles (Figs. 20, 21). The first is an equilateral triangle ABD with each side of length 2. Its angles are each of the same measure, namely, 60°. We bisect the angle at the top, getting the triangle ABC. The angle C is a right angle, the angle A is 60°, and the angle B is 30°.

The second figure is a right triangle with equal legs and consequently equal acute angles, each 45°.

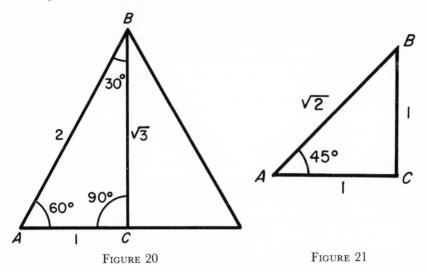

FIGURE 20   FIGURE 21

We readily calculate the lengths indicated on Figs. 20 and 21. From the figures:

$$\sin 30° = \sin \pi/6 = \tfrac{1}{2}$$
$$\sin 45° = \sin \pi/4 = \tfrac{1}{2}\sqrt{2}$$
$$\sin 60° = \sin \pi/3 = \tfrac{1}{2}\sqrt{3}$$
$$\cos 30° = \cos \pi/6 = \tfrac{1}{2}\sqrt{3}$$
$$\cos 45° = \cos \pi/4 = \tfrac{1}{2}\sqrt{2}$$
$$\cos 60° = \cos \pi/3 = \tfrac{1}{2}$$
$$\tan 30° = \tan \pi/6 = \tfrac{1}{3}\sqrt{3}$$
$$\tan 45° = \tan \pi/4 = 1$$
$$\tan 60° = \tan \pi/3 = \sqrt{3}$$
$$\cot 30° = \cot \pi/6 = \sqrt{3}$$
$$\cot 45° = \cot \pi/4 = 1$$
$$\cot 60° = \cot \pi/3 = \tfrac{1}{3}\sqrt{3}$$

The secants and cosecants are also readily obtained from the figures or as reciprocals of cosines and sines.

5. Trigonometric Functions of a Zero Angle, a Right Angle, a Straight Angle, a Revolution

No particular unit of angular measure is used in this section.

Draw figures for the respective four angles considered in standard position. The desired values then can be read off immediately.

sin 0 = 0

cos 0 = 1

sec 0 = 1

csc 0, undefined

tan 0 = 0

cot 0, undefined

sin (rt. ang.) = 1

cos (rt. ang.) = 0

sec (rt. ang.), undefined

csc (rt. ang.) = 1

tan (rt. ang.), undefined

cot (rt. ang.) = 0

sin (st. ang.) = 0

cos (st. ang.) = −1

sec (st. ang.) = −1

csc (st. ang.), undefined

tan (st. ang.) = 0

cot (st. ang.), undefined

sin (rev.) = 0

cos (rev.) = 1

sec (rev.) = 1

csc (rev.), undefined

tan (rev.) = 0

cot (rev.), undefined

6. *Functions of (180° ± α), Functions of (90° + α).* $\left[(\pi \pm \alpha), \left(\frac{\pi}{2} + \alpha\right)\right]$

Let α be positive and less than 90°.

Conclusions are readily drawn from Figs. 22 and 23.

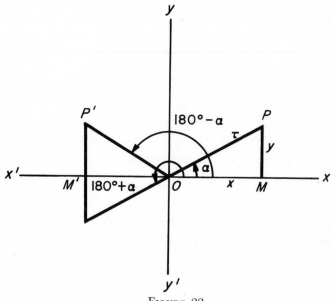

FIGURE 22

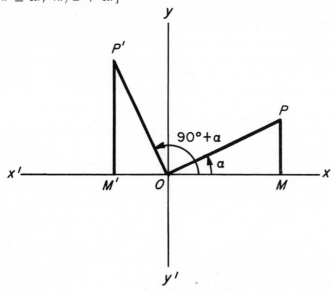

FIGURE 23

The triangles *OMP* and *OM'P'* are similar since an acute angle in the one is congruent to an acute angle in the other. Consequently in Fig. 22 we see that *M'P'/OP'* = *MP/OP*, etc. We have the following relations:

$$\sin (180° - \alpha) = \sin \alpha, \qquad \cos (180° - \alpha) = -\cos \alpha,$$
$$\sin (180° + \alpha) = -\sin \alpha, \qquad \cos (180° + \alpha) = -\cos \alpha,$$
$$\sin (90° + \alpha) = \cos \alpha, \qquad \cos (90° + \alpha) = -\sin \alpha.$$

There are similar relations for tan α, cot α, sec α, and csc α.

The student can draw figures with α lying in each of the four quadrants and convince himself that the above relations hold for any α. However, these and similar relations are demonstrated most easily in all generality by reference to the formulas of Chapter 7. Thus, $\sin (\pi - \alpha) = \sin \pi \cos \alpha - \cos \pi \sin \alpha$; but $\sin \pi = 0$, $\cos \pi = -1$. Hence

$$\sin (\pi - \alpha) = \sin \alpha.$$

We shall use this method later (see Chapter 7, par. 7).

EXERCISES

1. Express as functions of α.

(a) $\tan\left(\dfrac{\pi}{2} + \alpha\right)$, $\cot\left(\dfrac{\pi}{2} + \alpha\right)$, $\sec\left(\dfrac{\pi}{2} + \alpha\right)$, $\csc\left(\dfrac{\pi}{2} + \alpha\right)$.

(b) $\tan(180° - \alpha)$, $\cot(180° - \alpha)$, $\sec(180° - \alpha)$, $\csc(180° - \alpha)$.

(c) $\tan(180° + \alpha)$, $\cot(180° + \alpha)$, $\sec(180° + \alpha)$, $\csc(180° + \alpha)$.

(d) $\sin(2\pi + \alpha)$, $\cos(2\pi + \alpha)$, $\sec(2\pi + \alpha)$, $\csc(2\pi + \alpha)$.

(e) $\tan(\pi + \alpha)$, $\cot(\pi + \alpha)$, $\sec(\pi + \alpha)$, $\csc(\pi + \alpha)$.

2. Find $\sin 120°$, $\cos 210°$, $\tan 300°$, $\sin 300°$, $\sin 240°$, $\cos 240°$.

3. Find $\sin \frac{2}{3}\pi$, $\cos \frac{7}{6}\pi$, $\tan \frac{11}{6}\pi$.

4. What is the relation between the functions of zero and the functions of one revolution?

5. What is the relation between the functions of one revolution and the functions of two revolutions?

6. What is the relation between the functions of one right angle and the functions of five right angles?

7. Generalize the results you have given in the previous three exercises.

7. *Functions of Negative Angles*

We readily prove

$$\sin(-\alpha) = -\sin \alpha \qquad\qquad \cot(-\alpha) = -\cot \alpha,$$
$$\cos(-\alpha) = \cos \alpha \qquad\qquad \sec(-\alpha) = \sec \alpha,$$
$$\tan(-\alpha) = -\tan \alpha \qquad\qquad \csc(-\alpha) = -\csc \alpha.$$

This proof is easily given geometrically (however, we again refer to Chapter 7, par. 7).

Computation and Right Triangles

1. Computation

Most of numerical trigonometry is concerned with measured distances and angles and with values for trigonometric functions taken from tables. Measured distances and angles have already been discussed.[1] It is assumed that there is a distance (length) between each two objects. This distance is a number. The value used in numerical problems is a number that is determined by a measuring process which always could be carried out with greater precision than that used. If we say that a distance x is measured to be 2.5, we mean only that more precise measurement for x would get a value such that

$$2.45 < x < 2.55. \qquad (1)$$

There is no such thing as an exact measurement of distance. While consequently we should never use an equality mark in a relation such as

[1]See Chapters 1 and 3.

(1) involving measured distances, it is done in practice. When it is done both author and reader should understand what is meant. What we have said of measured distances holds with reference to measured angles. *There is no such thing as an exact value for a measured angle.*

Values given in the tables for the trigonometric functions are usually approximate. For example, if we find from a table that $y = 0.3553$, we interpret this to mean

$$0.35525 < y < 0.35535. \tag{2}$$

Now suppose that x is measured to be 2.5, as explained above, and that we wish to compute xy. We can multiply using inequalities (1) and (2).

0.35525	$<$	y	$<$	0.35535
2.45	$<$	x	$<$	2.55
177625				177675
142100				177675
71050				71070
0.8703625	$<$	xy	$<$	0.9061425

This inequality is all that we can tell about xy. Let us now calculate xy by formally multiplying together 2.5 and 0.3553. We get 0.88825. How absurd it would be to give it as an answer. It is customary in trigonometry courses to give 0.89.

In general, if x and y are approximate or measured numbers, and if $x + \delta$ and $y + \epsilon$ are more precise values, then

$$(x + \delta)(y + \epsilon) = xy + x\epsilon + y\delta + \delta\epsilon.$$

If δ and ϵ are small, we may drop $\delta\epsilon$ from consideration and say that the difference between xy and the more precise value is approximately not greater than the largest value that $|x\epsilon + y\delta|$ can have. In the above examples, $x = 2.5$, $y = 0.3553$, $|\delta| < 0.05$, and $|\epsilon| < 0.00005$. With these values, $|x\epsilon + y\delta| < |x\epsilon| + |y\delta| < 0.017$.

We have discussed the multiplication of two approximate numbers in some detail. Similar considerations apply to the product of three numbers.

$$(x+\delta)(y+\epsilon)(z+\eta) = xyz + xy\eta + xz\epsilon + yz\delta + \delta\epsilon z + \delta\eta y + \epsilon\eta x + \delta\epsilon\eta$$

Now if ϵ, δ, and η are small in comparison with x, y, z, the difference between *xyz* and the more precise product is approximately $xy\eta + xz\epsilon + yz\delta$. We determine the largest numerical value that this difference could possibly have and use it as an upper bound for the numerical value of the error.

Addition, subtraction, and division with approximate numbers or measurements are capable of the same kind of analysis.

The student will do well to remember than when, using the same approximate numbers, the number of arithmetical operations is increased, errors usually increase. If he is unable to analyze the error in detail, a working rule is:

Never retain more digits than can be guaranteed in the least accurate of the numbers used in a computation. If there are two or three operations, reduce the number of digits at least one below this number.

Frequently, a knowledge of the nature of the data will help greatly in estimating errors.

2. *Rounding Off Numbers*

If we know the first four digits of a number such as 0.1254, but only wish to write three, we write 0.125 since the last digit is less than 5. On the other hand, if we know the first four digits to be 0.1257 but only wish to write three digits, we write 0.126 since the last digit is more than 5. If we know the first four digits only but wish to write three and if the last digit is 5, some people follow the rule of making the last digit even. Thus, 0.1255 is written 0.126 0.1265 also is written 0.126.

EXERCISES

1. Take the measured values 2.76, 3.05, and 7.123. Multiply them together and discuss the reliability of your answer.
2. Add the numbers of Exercise 1 and discuss the reliability of your answer.
3. Divide 3.05 by 7.123 and discuss the reliability of your answer.
4. Can the mathematician discuss a problem in which 3.05 and 7.123 are distances and treat them as exact numbers?

3. *The Solution of Right Triangles*

Let us consider a right triangle ABC (see Fig. 24).

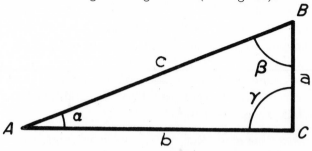

FIGURE 24

Here we denote by α, β, and γ the positive measures of the angles of the triangle as indicated in the figure. We also denote the lengths of the sides of the triangle by a, b, c as indicated. In most trigonometry books the measure of the angle at A is simply indicated by A. This practice is convenient, and we shall not hesitate to follow it when no ambiguity is introduced. Thus, $A = \alpha$, $B = \beta$, $C = \gamma$ = a right angle. Now if we are given two of the five quantities a, b, c, α, β, provided that at least one of them is the length of a side, then we are able to calculate the remaining ones of the quantities a, b, c, α, β. This calculation is what is meant by **solving the triangle.** The process is best described by means of illustrative examples.

Example 1:   Given $c = 10$, $A = \alpha = 30°$, find the measures of the other parts of the triangle (see Fig. 24).

Solution:

$$a = 10 \sin 30° = 10 \cdot \tfrac{1}{2} = 5$$
$$b = 10 \cos 30° = 10 \cdot \tfrac{1}{2}\sqrt{3} = 5\sqrt{3}$$
$$B = 90 - A = 60°.$$

Example 2:   Given $a = 10.00$, $A = 30°$, find the measures of the other parts of the triangle (again see Fig. 24).

Solution:

$$B = 90° - A = 60°$$
$$b = a \tan B = 10\sqrt{3}$$
$$c = a \csc A = \frac{a}{\sin A} = \frac{10}{0.5} = 20.00.$$

We also can find readily c by the Pythagorean Theorem.

$$c^2 = a^2 + b^2$$
$$c^2 = 100 + 300 = 400$$
$$c = 20.$$

Example 3: Given $c = 45.00$, $A = 35°$, find the measures of the other parts of the triangle.

Solution: Use table.

$$B = 90° - 35° = 55°$$
$$a = 45 \sin 35° = 25.81$$
$$b = 45 \cos 35° = 36.86.$$

Example 4: At noon the shadow of a flagpole is measured to be 36.2 feet long. The angle of elevation of the sun is measured to be 57°. How tall is the flagpole?

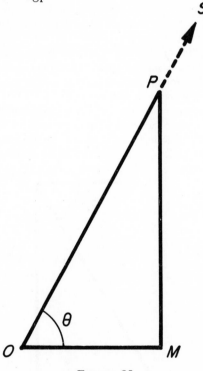

FIGURE 25

The term **angle of elevation** refers to θ as indicated in Fig. 25.

$$\theta = 57°$$
$$OM = 36.2.$$

Solution: Use table.

$$MP = OM \tan 57° = (36.2) \cdot (1.5399) = 55.7.$$

EXERCISES

Solve the right triangles in exercises 1 to 6. In all instances c is the length of the hypotenuse, A and B are acute angles, a is the length of the side opposite A, and b is the length of the side opposite B.

1. $a = 25$, $A = 15° 13'$.
2. $c = 1000$, $a = 354$.
3. $c = 1000$, $B = 17° 26'$.
4. $c = 525$, $A = 57° 42'$.
5. $c = 732.3$, $b = 125.2$.
6. $a = 421$, $b = 176.2$.
7. A ladder 35 feet long is leaning against a house on a level lot. Its foot is ten feet from the house. How high above the ground is the top of the ladder? What angle does it make with the ground?
8. A tower 100 feet tall is on the bank of a river. From a point on the bank of the river directly opposite the tower the angle of elevation of the top of the tower is found to be 34° 15'. How wide is the river?
9. A highway runs up a hill at a constant angle of 5°. What is the difference in elevation of two points on the highway 500 feet apart measured along the highway?
10. From the top of a tower the **angle of depression** of an object 100 feet from its foot is found to be 72°. How high is the tower? (In Fig. 26, OT is tower and P is object.)

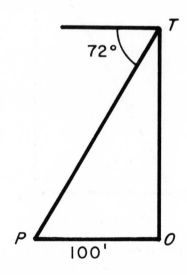

FIGURE 26

11. If the angle of elevation of the sun is 28° 14′, how long is the shadow of a man 6 feet 2 inches tall standing on a level court?

12. The length of a tightly stretched kite string is 600 feet. It makes an angle of 34° with the horizontal. How high is the kite?

13. Find the length of the chord of a circle of 4 foot radius if it subtends an angle of 40° at the center of the circle.

14. At a point 12 feet from the center of a circle of radius 8 feet, tangents are drawn to the circle. Find the angle between them.

15. Assuming the Earth a sphere of radius 3960 miles, find how far a point on the Earth's surface of latitude 30° is from the Earth's axis.

16. What angle does the diagonal of a cube make with the edges of the cube?

17. Two ships leave the same wharf at the same time. One sails directly south at the constant rate of 25 miles per hour. The other sails directly east at the constant rate of 20 miles per hour. How far apart are they at the end of one-half hour?

Chapter 6

Elementary Identities

1. Examples

From the definition of the trigonometric functions it follows that for all permissible values of α

$$\sec \alpha = \frac{1}{\cos \alpha}, \tag{1}$$

$$\csc \alpha = \frac{1}{\sin \alpha}, \tag{2}$$

$$\cot \alpha = \frac{1}{\tan \alpha}. \tag{3}$$

From the Pythagorean theorem

$$x^2 + y^2 = r^2.$$

Hence

$$\left(\frac{x}{r}\right)^2 + \left(\frac{y}{r}\right)^2 = 1,$$

$$1 + \left(\frac{y}{x}\right)^2 = \left(\frac{r}{x}\right)^2, \qquad x \neq 0,$$

$$\left(\frac{x}{y}\right)^2 + 1 = \left(\frac{r}{y}\right)^2, \qquad y \neq 0.$$

These three relations can be written

$$\sin^2\alpha + \cos^2\alpha = 1, \tag{4}$$
$$1 + \tan^2\alpha = \sec^2\alpha, \tag{5}$$
$$\cot^2\alpha + 1 = \csc^2\alpha. \tag{6}$$

Here we may have any value of α for which all functions entering the formula are defined. We call formulas (1), (2), (3), (4), (5), and (6) the **fundamental elementary identities.** It is frequently possible to use these fundamental identities to prove more complicated identities, and it is surprising how frequently this has to be done in mathematics. The situation is somewhat analogous to the simplification of complicated expressions in elementary algebra. The methods are best illustrated by examples.

Example 1: Prove the identity

$$\frac{\cos^2\alpha}{1 - \sin \alpha} = 1 + \sin \alpha, \qquad 1 - \sin \alpha \neq 0.$$

We immediately notice that if $1 - \sin \alpha = 0$ the lefthand member could not possibly equal the righthand member because the denominator in the lefthand member is zero and we cannot divide by zero.

First Proof

From the fundamental identities,

$$\cos^2\alpha = 1 - \sin^2\alpha.$$

Hence

$$\frac{\cos^2\alpha}{1 - \sin \alpha} = \frac{1 - \sin^2\alpha}{1 - \sin \alpha}, \qquad 1 - \sin \alpha \neq 0$$

$$\frac{\cos^2\alpha}{1 - \sin \alpha} = \frac{(1 - \sin \alpha)(1 + \sin \alpha)}{1 - \sin \alpha}$$

$$\frac{\cos^2\alpha}{1 - \sin \alpha} = 1 + \sin \alpha$$

which is what we wished to establish.

"False Proof"

$$\frac{\cos^2\alpha}{1 - \sin\alpha} = 1 + \sin\alpha, \qquad 1 - \sin\alpha \neq 0. \tag{7}$$

Clear the equation of fractions by multiplying through by $1 - \sin\alpha$.

$$\cos^2\alpha = (1 + \sin\alpha)(1 - \sin\alpha)$$
$$\cos^2\alpha = 1 - \sin^2\alpha$$
$$\cos^2\alpha = \cos^2\alpha \tag{8}$$

which is true. Hence (7) is true.

What is the matter with this? Let us discuss it. We start with (7). We do not know whether it is true or false. We arrive at (8) by correct reasoning. We know (8) to be true. From this fact we cannot conclude that (7) is true. False hypotheses frequently lead to true conclusions. An example from arithmetic where a false hypothesis leads to a correct conclusion is the following.

Let us prove that $-1 = 1$.

$$-1 = 1. \tag{9}$$

Square both sides.

$$1 = 1. \tag{10}$$

Now (10) is correct. Of course this does not mean that (9) is correct. More elaborate examples are easy to construct. As example (2) we give such an illustration involving trigonometric functions.

Second Proof

$$\cos^2\alpha = \cos^2\alpha \tag{11}$$
$$\cos^2\alpha = 1 - \sin^2\alpha$$
$$\cos^2\alpha = (1 - \sin\alpha)(1 + \sin\alpha).$$
$$\frac{\cos^2\alpha}{1 - \sin\alpha} = 1 + \sin\alpha, \qquad 1 - \sin\alpha \neq 0. \tag{12}$$

Now the difference between the reasoning here and the reasoning under "false proof" is that we start with a correct identity, namely (11), and arrive at (12) by means of correct steps. It is true that "false proof" may have suggested the steps of second proof. This is the case in many problems. If the student goes through a process such as "false proof," he must be sure that all steps can be made in reverse order (that he can retrace his steps) and in only one way.

Third Proof

Let us assume that

$$\frac{\cos^2\alpha}{1 - \sin\alpha} \neq 1 + \sin\alpha \qquad \text{when } 1 - \sin\alpha \neq 0.$$

Then multiplying both sides of this equation by $1 - \sin\alpha$ we get

$$\cos^2\alpha \neq 1 - \sin^2\alpha \quad \text{or} \quad \cos^2\alpha + \sin^2\alpha \neq 1.$$

But $\cos^2\alpha + \sin^2\alpha = 1$. Hence the hypothesis must have been wrong. Hence it must be true that

$$\frac{\cos^2\alpha}{1 - \sin\alpha} = 1 - \sin\alpha, \qquad 1 - \sin\alpha \neq 0.$$

Example 2: A more elaborate example of a false hypothesis that leads to a correct conclusion is the following: Prove

$$(\tan\alpha)(\sin\alpha) = \cos\alpha - \sec\alpha. \qquad (13)$$

Square both sides.

$$(\tan^2\alpha)(\sin^2\alpha) = \cos^2\alpha - 2\cos\alpha\sec\alpha + \sec^2\alpha.$$

But $\cos\alpha\sec\alpha = 1$ and $\sin^2\alpha = 1 - \cos^2\alpha$. Hence

$$(\tan^2\alpha)(1 - \cos^2\alpha) = \cos^2\alpha - 2 + \sec^2\alpha \qquad (14)$$
$$\tan^2\alpha - \sin^2\alpha = \cos^2\alpha - 2 + \sec^2\alpha.$$

Transpose all terms to the right hand member. We get

$$0 = (\cos^2\alpha + \sin^2\alpha) + (\sec^2\alpha - \tan^2\alpha) - 2.$$

But $\cos^2\alpha + \sin^2\alpha = 1$ and $\sec^2\alpha - \tan^2\alpha = 1$.
Hence

$$0 = 0. \qquad (15)$$

This is, of course, true. However, (13), with which we started, is false in general. To show this let α be positive and small. We know that $\sin\alpha$, $\cos\alpha$, $\tan\alpha$, and $\sec\alpha$ are all positive and that $\cos\alpha < 1$ and $\sec\alpha \geq 1$. It results that the lefthand member of (13) is positive while the righthand member is negative. The two members then are not equal.

Example 3: Prove

$$(\tan\alpha)(\sin\alpha) = \sec\alpha - \cos\alpha, \qquad \cos\alpha \neq 0. \qquad (16)$$

Now $\tan \alpha = \sin \alpha / \cos \alpha$ and $\sec \alpha = 1/\cos \alpha$. The first member of (14) then reduces as follows:

$$(\tan \alpha)(\sin \alpha) = (\sin \alpha / \cos \alpha) \sin \alpha = \sin^2 \alpha / \cos \alpha.$$

The second member takes the following form:

$$\sec \alpha - \cos \alpha = \frac{1}{\cos \alpha} - \cos \alpha = \frac{1 - \cos^2 \alpha}{\cos \alpha} = \frac{\sin^2 \alpha}{\cos \alpha}.$$

Thus each member is separately reduced to $\sin^2 \alpha / \cos \alpha$. The two members of (16) are then equal and the identity is correct. Notice that we assumed $\cos \alpha \neq 0$. This assumption is necessary since when $\cos \alpha = 0$ neither $\sec \alpha$ nor $\tan \alpha$ is defined.

Example 4:   Prove the identity:

$$\frac{\sec \alpha + \csc \alpha}{1 + \tan \alpha} = \csc \alpha, \qquad \cos \alpha \neq 0, \sin \alpha \neq 0, 1 + \tan \alpha \neq 0. \quad (17)$$

Consider the lefthand member of (17). Multiply numerator and denominator by $\csc \alpha$.

$$\frac{\sec \alpha + \csc \alpha}{1 + \tan \alpha} = \frac{(\sec \alpha + \csc \alpha)\csc \alpha}{\csc \alpha + (\tan \alpha)(\csc \alpha)}.$$

But

$$\tan \alpha \csc \alpha = \frac{\sin \alpha}{\cos \alpha} \cdot \frac{1}{\sin \alpha} = \frac{1}{\cos \alpha} = \sec \alpha.$$

Hence

$$\frac{\sec \alpha + \csc \alpha}{1 + \tan \alpha} = \frac{(\sec \alpha + \csc \alpha)\csc \alpha}{\csc \alpha + \sec \alpha} = \csc \alpha,$$

which is what we wished to prove.

2. Comparison of Examples 2 and 3

The student has noticed that (13) and (16) differ only in sign of the righthand member. The first thing that we did under Example 2 was to square both sides of (13). We would have obtained the same result, namely (14), had we started with the correct (16) instead of the incorrect (13). Now if we try to reverse the steps under Example 2, namely begin with the correct (15) and work upward when we reach (14), we do not know whether to write the correct (16) or the incorrect (13).

Squaring is an operation where there is only one answer. For instance, we square 3 and get 9, square 4 and get 16, etc. However, consider the reverse operation: If $x^2 = 9$, then $x = 3$ or -3. Thus when we try to retrace steps through squaring there are two paths. Retrace steps under Example 2 and a path is taken which leads to an incorrect statement, namely (13).

As the student advances in his mathematics he will encounter numerous other operations that do not have a unique reversal.

EXERCISES

Establish that the following are identities for all values of α that give meaning to the expressions which enter the equation.

1. $\sin \alpha \cot \alpha = \cos \alpha$.

2. $\cos \alpha \tan \alpha = \sin \alpha$.

3. $\tan \alpha = \sin \alpha \sec \alpha$.

4. $\tan \alpha / \sin \alpha = \sec \alpha$.

5. $\dfrac{1 - \sin^2\alpha}{\sin^2\alpha} = \cot^2\alpha$.

6. $\dfrac{\cos \alpha}{1 + \sin \alpha} = \dfrac{1 - \sin \alpha}{\cos \alpha}$.

7. $\dfrac{1 - \cos \alpha}{1 + \cos \alpha} = (\csc \alpha - \cot \alpha)^2$.

8. $\dfrac{\csc^2\alpha - 1}{\sec^2\alpha - 1} = \cot^4\alpha$.

9. $\dfrac{\sin \alpha}{\sec \alpha} = \dfrac{1}{\tan \alpha + \cot \alpha}$.

10. $\cot \alpha \csc \alpha = \dfrac{1}{\sec \alpha - \cos \alpha}$.

11. $\csc^4\alpha - \cot^4\alpha = \csc^2\alpha + \cot^2\alpha$.

12. $(\tan \alpha + \cot \alpha)^2 = \sec^2\alpha + \cot^2\alpha$.

13. $(1 + \sec \alpha)(1 - \cos \alpha) = \sec \alpha / \csc^2\alpha$.

14. $\dfrac{\sec\alpha + 1}{\tan\alpha} = \dfrac{\tan\alpha}{\sec\alpha - 1}.$

15. $\cos^4\alpha - \sin^4\alpha = 1 - 2\sin^2\alpha.$

16. $\dfrac{1 + \cot\alpha}{\csc\alpha} = \dfrac{1 + \tan\alpha}{\sec\alpha}.$

17. $\dfrac{1}{1 - \cos\alpha} + \dfrac{1}{1 + \cos\alpha} = 2(1 + \cot^2\alpha).$

18. $\dfrac{1 + \cot\alpha}{\csc\alpha} = \dfrac{1 + \tan\alpha}{\sec\alpha}.$

19. $\dfrac{1 - \cot\alpha}{\csc\alpha} = \dfrac{\tan\alpha - 1}{\sec\alpha}.$

20. $\dfrac{1 + \sin^2\alpha\,\sec^2\alpha}{1 + \cos^2\alpha\,\csc^2\alpha} = \tan^2\alpha.$

21. $\dfrac{\cos\alpha - \sin\alpha}{\cos\alpha + \sin\alpha} = \dfrac{1 - \tan\alpha}{1 + \tan\alpha}.$

22. $\dfrac{\tan\alpha + \sin\alpha}{\csc\alpha + \cot\alpha} = \sin^2\alpha\,\sec\alpha.$

23. $\csc^2\alpha - (1 + \cos^2\alpha) = \cos^2\alpha + \cot^2\alpha.$
24. $(1 - \cos\alpha)(1 + \sec\alpha) = \sin^2\alpha/\cos\alpha.$

Addition Formulas in Trigonometry

1. Fundamental Formulas

It is true that

$$a(b + c) = ab + ac,$$

where a, b, c are any numbers. It is *not* true in general that

$$\sqrt{a^2 + b^2} = a + b.$$

We mean by this statement that this formula is not true for every a and b. For what values of a and b is it true? Let the student answer. Likewise it is *not* true in general that

$$\sin(\alpha + \beta) = \sin \alpha + \sin \beta$$

or that

$$\cos(\alpha + \beta) = \cos \alpha + \cos \beta.$$

For example, if $\alpha = \pi/6$ and $\beta = \pi/3$ then $\alpha + \beta = \pi/2$ and

$$\sin \pi/2 \neq \sin \pi/6 + \sin \pi/3$$

since $\sin \pi/2 = 1$, $\sin \pi/6 = 1/2$ and $\sin \pi/3 = \sqrt{3}/2$. We desire rules by which we can calculate $\sin (\alpha + \beta)$, $\cos (\alpha + \beta)$, and so forth, if we know $\sin \alpha$, $\sin \beta$, $\cos \alpha$ and $\cos \beta$. Such rules prove to be of the greatest importance in mathematics. The formulas which give these rules and which we shall prove are:

$$\cos (\alpha + \beta) = \cos \alpha \cos \beta - \sin \alpha \sin \beta \qquad (1)$$
$$\cos (\alpha - \beta) = \cos \alpha \cos \beta + \sin \alpha \sin \beta \qquad (2)$$
$$\sin (\alpha + \beta) = \sin \alpha \cos \beta + \cos \alpha \sin \beta \qquad (3)$$
$$\sin (\alpha - \beta) = \sin \alpha \cos \beta - \cos \alpha \sin \beta. \qquad (4)$$

Such formulas are called **addition formulas.**

2. *Distance Formula*

Before proving the above important relations we shall establish a formula from analytic geometry. Given two points $P_1(x_1, y_1)$ and $P_2(x_2, y_2)$ we wish a formula for the positive distance between them. We draw two figures, namely Figs. 27 and 28. The student can draw additional figures if he likes.

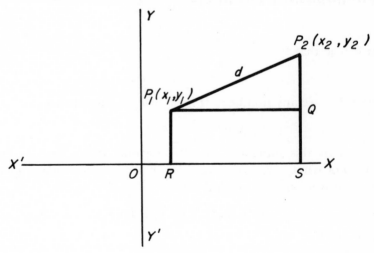

FIGURE 27

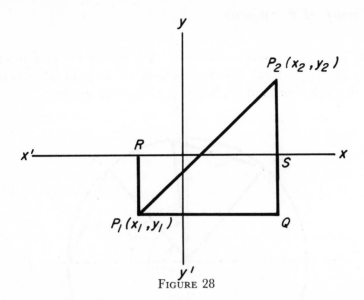

FIGURE 28

The line segment P_1Q is parallel to the x-axis and QP_2 to the y-axis. Then $P_1Q = x_2 - x$; $QP_2 = y_2 - y_1$. Hence, if d is the required positive distance, by the Pythagorean Theorem

$$d = \sqrt{(x_2 - x_1)^2 + (y_2 - y_1)^2}.$$

We call this the **distance formula.**

Example 1:   Find the distance between the points $(1, 4)$ and $(-2, 7)$.

$$d = \sqrt{(-2 - 1)^2 + (7 - 4)^2} = 3\sqrt{2}.$$

Example 2:   Find the length of the line segment connecting $(-3, 7)$ and $(1, 8)$.

$$d = \sqrt{(1 + 3)^2 + (8 - 7)^2} = \sqrt{17}.$$

EXERCISES

1. Find the distance between the following points: (a) $(2, 3)$ and $(8, -2)$; (b) $\left(\dfrac{a + b}{2}, \dfrac{a - b}{2}\right)$ and (a, b); (c) $(c^2 + d^2, cd)$ and $(2c - d, c - d)$.

2. Find the distance between the points $(\cos \alpha, \cos \beta)$ and $(1, 0)$.

3. Find the distance between the two points $(\cos \beta, \sin \beta)$ and $(\cos \alpha, \sin \alpha)$.

4. Prove that the following three points are the vertices of a right triangle $(1, 2)$, $(7, 8)$, $(2, 1)$.

5. Prove that the following four points are vertices of a rhombus: $(1, 1)$, $(6, 6)$, $(11, 1)$, $(6, -4)$. What is a rhombus?

3. *Proof of Formulas*

We now return to our main problem, namely the establishment of formulas (1), (2), (3), (4). The method we use lacks in motivation. However, it is short and applies to angles of any measure.

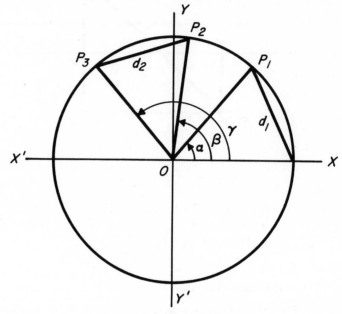

FIGURE 29

We begin by drawing a unit circle about the origin, that is a circle of radius 1. Let α and β be any angles and let $\gamma = \alpha + \beta$. We mark the points P_1, P_2, and P_3 as indicated in the figure. The coordinates of P_1 are $(\cos \alpha, \sin \alpha)$. The coordinates of P_2 are $(\cos \beta, \sin \beta)$. The coordinates of P_3 are $(\cos \gamma, \sin \gamma)$.

$$d_1 = \sqrt{(\cos \alpha - 1)^2 + (\sin \alpha)^2}$$
$$d_2 = \sqrt{(\cos \beta - \cos \gamma)^2 + (\sin \beta - \sin \gamma)^2}.$$

However, $d_1 = d_2$. This is true since each is a chord subtended by an angle, the measure of which is $\gamma - \beta = \alpha$. Consequently

$$\sqrt{(\cos \alpha - 1)^2 + (\sin \alpha)^2} = \sqrt{(\cos \beta - \cos \gamma)^2 + (\sin \beta - \sin \gamma)^2}.$$

Squaring both sides and performing other indicated operations we have:

$\cos^2\alpha - 2\cos\alpha + 1 + \sin^2\alpha = \cos^2\beta - 2\cos\beta\cos\gamma + \cos^2\gamma + \sin^2\beta$
$- 2\sin\beta\sin\gamma + \sin^2\gamma.$
But $\sin^2\alpha + \cos^2\alpha = 1$, $\sin^2\beta + \cos^2\beta = 1$, and $\sin^2\gamma + \cos^2\gamma = 1$.

Hence

$$1 - \cos\alpha = 1 - \cos\beta\cos\gamma - \sin\beta\sin\gamma.$$

From this, since $\alpha = \gamma - \beta$,

$$\cos(\gamma - \beta) = \cos\gamma\cos\beta + \sin\beta\sin\gamma.$$

This is formula (2). It holds for any angles positive or negative. Now replace $-\beta$ by β' and remember that $\sin(-\beta') = -\sin\beta'$ and $\cos(-\beta') = \cos\beta'$ and then drop the primes and we have $\cos(\gamma + \beta) = \cos\gamma\cos\beta - \sin\gamma\sin\beta$. This is formula (1). Now $\sin(\gamma + \delta) = \cos(\frac{\pi}{2} - (\gamma + \delta)) = \cos[(\frac{\pi}{2} - \gamma) - \delta] = \cos(\frac{\pi}{2} - \gamma)$ $\cos\delta + \sin(\frac{\pi}{2} - \gamma)\sin\delta = \sin\gamma\cos\delta + \cos\gamma\sin\delta$. This is formula (3). Replace δ by $-\delta'$ and then drop the prime and we obtain formula (4). This completes proof of the fundamental set of formulas (1), (2), (3), and (4). The fact that in our results different letters occur is of no consequence. To get (1) and (2), as written, replace γ by α. To get (3) and (4) as written replace γ by α and δ by β.

We next wish to find formulas for $\tan(\alpha + \beta)$. We know that

$$\tan(\alpha + \beta) = \frac{\sin(\alpha + \beta)}{\cos(\alpha + \beta)} = \frac{\sin\alpha\cos\beta + \cos\alpha\sin\beta}{\cos\alpha\cos\beta - \sin\alpha\sin\beta}.$$

Divide numerator and denominator by $\cos\alpha\cos\beta$ and we get the desired formula.

$$\tan(\alpha + \beta) = \frac{\tan\alpha + \tan\beta}{1 - \tan\alpha\tan\beta}, \tag{5}$$
$$1 - \tan\alpha\tan\beta \neq 0, \quad \cos\alpha \neq 0, \quad \cos\beta \neq 0$$

Similarly

$$\tan(\alpha - \beta) = \frac{\tan\alpha - \tan\beta}{1 + \tan\alpha\tan\beta}, \tag{6}$$
$$1 + \tan\alpha\tan\beta \neq 0, \quad \cos\alpha \neq 0, \quad \cos\beta \neq 0$$

and

$$\cot(\alpha + \beta) = \frac{\cot\alpha\cot\beta - 1}{\cot\alpha + \cot\beta}, \tag{7}$$
$$\cot\alpha + \cot\beta \neq 0, \quad \sin\alpha \neq 0, \quad \sin\beta \neq 0$$

and

$$\cot(\alpha - \beta) = \frac{\cot \alpha \cot \beta + 1}{\cot \beta - \cot \alpha}, \tag{8}$$

$$\cot \beta - \cot \alpha \neq 0, \quad \sin \alpha \neq 0, \quad \sin \beta \neq 0.$$

Formulas (1), (2), (3), (4), (5), (6), (7), and (8) are called **addition formulas.**

EXERCISES

1. Prove formula (6) in detail.
2. Prove formulas (7) and (8).
3. Express $\csc(\alpha + \beta)$ in terms of $\csc \alpha$, $\csc \beta$, $\sec \alpha$, and $\sec \beta$.
4. Express $\sec(\alpha + \beta)$ in terms of $\sec \alpha$, $\sec \beta$, $\csc \alpha$, and $\csc \beta$.
5. Take your table and look up sine and cosine of 0.3333 and of 0.6667. Use these values to find approximate values for $\sin 1$ and $\cos 1$. Here, of course, we are using radian measure.
6. Take your table and look up $\tan 0.85$ and $\tan 0.15$, then calculate $\tan 1$ approximately.
7. Are any of the following correct identities?

$$\sin(A + B) = \sin A + \sin B.$$
$$\cos(A - B) = \cos A + \cos B.$$
$$\tan(A + B) = \tan A + \tan B.$$

8. If $\sin x = 0.3$, is $x = 0.3/\sin$?

Prove the following identities. Note that no identity has meaning if a denominator vanishes; also note that neither $\tan \alpha$ nor $\sec \alpha$ is defined if $\cos \alpha = 0$ and that neither $\cot \alpha$ nor $\csc \alpha$ is defined if $\sin \alpha = 0$.

9. $\sin(\alpha + \beta)\sin(\alpha - \beta) = \sin^2\alpha - \sin^2\beta = \cos^2\beta - \cos^2\alpha.$
10. $\cos(\alpha + \beta)\cos(\alpha - \beta) = \cos^2\alpha - \sin^2\beta = \cos^2\beta - \sin^2\alpha.$

11. $\dfrac{\sin(\alpha + \beta) + \sin(\alpha - \beta)}{\cos(\alpha + \beta) + \cos(\alpha - \beta)} = \tan \alpha.$

12. $\dfrac{\sin(\alpha + \beta)}{\sin(\alpha - \beta)} = \dfrac{\tan \alpha + \tan \beta}{\tan \alpha - \tan \beta}.$

13. $\sec(\alpha - \beta) = \dfrac{\sec \alpha \sec \beta}{1 + \tan \alpha \tan \beta}.$

14. $\dfrac{\tan \alpha + \tan \beta}{1 - \tan \alpha \tan \beta} \cdot \dfrac{\cot \alpha \cot \beta - 1}{\cot \alpha + \cot \beta} = 1.$

15. $\sin(A + B) + \cos(A - B) = (\cos A + \sin A)(\cos B + \sin B).$
16. $\sin(A + B) \sec A \sec B = \tan A + \tan B.$

4. *Trigonometric Functions of 2α, 3α, and 4α*

If we replace β by α in (3) we have:

$$\sin(\alpha + \alpha) = \sin \alpha \cos \alpha + \cos \alpha \sin \alpha.$$

Hence,

$$\sin 2\alpha = 2 \sin \alpha \cos \alpha. \tag{9}$$

If we replace β by α in formula (1) we have:

$$\cos 2\alpha = \cos^2\alpha - \sin^2\alpha. \tag{10}$$

Moreover $\sin^2\alpha + \cos^2\alpha = 1$. We can substitute from this in (10) obtaining the following two forms:

$$\cos 2\alpha = 2 \cos^2\alpha - 1; \tag{11}$$

$$\cos 2\alpha = 1 - 2 \sin^2\alpha. \tag{12}$$

We thus have three formulas for $\cos 2\alpha$, namely (10), (11), and (12). By means of the numerous identities involving the trigonometric functions still further forms could be obtained should we so desire.

Letting $\beta = \alpha$ in (5) we obtain a formula for $\tan 2\alpha$:

$$\tan 2\alpha = \frac{2 \tan \alpha}{1 - \tan^2\alpha}. \tag{13}$$

Of course for (13) to have meaning it is necessary that α have a value for which $\tan \alpha$ is defined and that $1 - \tan^2\alpha \neq 0$.

Formulas for $\sin 3\alpha$ and $\cos 3\alpha$ can be obtained as follows:

$$\sin(3\alpha) = \sin(\alpha + 2\alpha) = \sin \alpha \cos 2\alpha + \cos \alpha \sin 2\alpha. \tag{14}$$

Let us now substitute in (14) from (9) and (12). We get:

$$\begin{aligned}
\sin 3\alpha &= \sin \alpha(1 - 2 \sin^2\alpha) + \cos \alpha(2 \sin \alpha \cos \alpha) \qquad (15) \\
&= \sin \alpha - 2 \sin^3\alpha + 2 \sin \alpha \cos^2\alpha \\
&= \sin \alpha - 2 \sin^3\alpha + 2(\sin \alpha)(1 - \sin^2\alpha) \\
&= 3 \sin \alpha - 4 \sin^3\alpha.
\end{aligned}$$

Similarly,

$$\begin{aligned}
\cos 3\alpha &= \cos \alpha \cos 2\alpha - \sin \alpha \sin 2\alpha \\
&= 4 \cos^3\alpha - 3 \cos \alpha.
\end{aligned}$$

In a similar manner we can find formulas for $\sin 4\alpha$ and $\cos 4\alpha$. Thus,

$$\sin 4\alpha = 2 \sin 2\alpha \cos 2\alpha$$
$$= 4 \sin\alpha \cos^3\alpha - 4 \sin^3\alpha\cos \alpha.$$

Similarly,

$$\cos 4\alpha = 8 \cos^4\alpha - 8 \cos^2\alpha + 1.$$

Continuing this process formulas for $\sin n\alpha$ and $\cos n\alpha$ when $n > 4$ can be obtained. Formulas for functions of 2α, 3α, and 4α are written together for ready reference.

$$\sin 2\alpha = 2 \sin \alpha \cos \alpha. \tag{16}$$
$$\cos 2\alpha = \cos^2\alpha - \sin^2\alpha. \tag{17}$$
$$\cos 2\alpha = 2 \cos^2\alpha - 1. \tag{18}$$
$$\cos 2\alpha = 1 - 2 \sin^2\alpha. \tag{19}$$
$$\tan 2\alpha = \frac{2 \tan \alpha}{1 - \tan^2\alpha}. \tag{20}$$
$$\sin 3\alpha = 3 \sin \alpha - 4 \sin^3\alpha. \tag{21}$$
$$\cos 3\alpha = 4 \cos^3\alpha - 3 \cos \alpha. \tag{22}$$
$$\sin 4\alpha = 4 \sin \alpha \cos {}^3\alpha - 4 \sin^3\alpha \cos \alpha. \tag{23}$$
$$\cos 4\alpha = 8 \cos^4\alpha - 8 \cos^2\alpha + 1. \tag{24}$$

5. *Trigonometric Functions of $\frac{1}{2}\alpha$*

In formulas (19) and (18) replace α by β. Then let $2\beta = \alpha$. We can do this since α represents any angle. We have

$$\cos \alpha = 1 - 2 \sin^2 \tfrac{1}{2}\alpha$$

and

$$\cos \alpha = 2 \cos^2 \tfrac{1}{2}\alpha - 1$$

Solve these for $\sin \frac{1}{2}\alpha$ and $\cos \frac{1}{2}\alpha$. Divide $\sin \frac{1}{2}\alpha$ by $\cos \frac{1}{2}\alpha$ to obtain $\tan \frac{1}{2}\alpha$. We get the following three formulas:

$$\sin \frac{1}{2}\alpha = \pm\sqrt{\frac{1 - \cos \alpha}{2}}; \tag{25}$$

$$\cos \frac{1}{2}\alpha = \pm\sqrt{\frac{1 + \cos \alpha}{2}}, \tag{26}$$

$$\tan \frac{1}{2}\alpha = \pm\sqrt{\frac{1 - \cos \alpha}{1 + \cos \alpha}}, \quad 1 + \cos \alpha \neq 0. \tag{27}$$

We use the plus or minus sign according to the quadrant in which $\frac{1}{2}\alpha$ lies.

EXERCISES

1. If $\sin \alpha = \frac{1}{2}$ and $\cos \alpha = \frac{1}{2}\sqrt{3}$, work out $\sin 2\alpha$, $\cos 2\alpha$ and $\tan 2\alpha$.
2. Look up $\sin \frac{1}{2}$ and $\cos \frac{1}{2}$ and then work out $\sin 1$ and $\cos 1$.
3. If $\sin \alpha = \frac{1}{3}$ and $\cos \alpha = -\frac{2}{3}\sqrt{2}$, work out $\sin 3\alpha$ and $\cos 3\alpha$.
4. Look up $\sin \frac{1}{10}$ and $\cos \frac{1}{10}$ and then work out $\sin \frac{4}{10}$ and $\cos \frac{4}{10}$.
5. If $\cos \alpha = \frac{1}{2}$, work out $\sin \frac{1}{2}\alpha$, $\cos \frac{1}{2}\alpha$ and $\tan \frac{1}{2}\alpha$. Leave signs in your answer.
6. Look up $\cos 1$ in your table and with this value work out $\sin \frac{1}{2}$, $\cos \frac{1}{2}$, and $\tan \frac{1}{2}$.

Prove the following relations true for values of α which give them meaning.

7. $\cos^4\alpha - \sin^4\alpha = \cos 2\alpha$.
8. $\tan \alpha + \cot \alpha = 2 \csc 2\alpha$.
9. $\cot 2\alpha = \csc 4\alpha + \cot 4\alpha$.

10. $\frac{1}{2} \sin 2\alpha = \dfrac{\tan \alpha}{1 + \tan^2\alpha}$.

11. $\cos \alpha = \dfrac{1 - \tan^2 \frac{1}{2}\alpha}{1 + \tan^2 \frac{1}{2}\alpha}$.

12. $\sin \alpha = \dfrac{2 \tan \frac{1}{2}\alpha}{1 + \tan^2 \frac{1}{2}\alpha}$.

13. $\dfrac{\sin \alpha + \sin 2\alpha}{1 + \cos \alpha + \cos 2\alpha} = \tan \alpha$.

14. $\tan 2\alpha = \dfrac{2}{\cot \alpha - \tan \alpha}$.

15. $\cot \frac{1}{2}\alpha - \tan \frac{1}{2}\alpha = 2 \cot \alpha$.
16. $2 \cos \alpha \csc 2\alpha = \csc \alpha$.
17. $\sin 3\alpha/\sin \alpha - \cos 3\alpha/\cos \alpha = 2$.

18. $\dfrac{\cos 3\alpha}{\sin \alpha} + \dfrac{\sin 3\alpha}{\cos \alpha} = 2 \cot 2\alpha$.

19. $\sin^2 2\alpha \cos^2 2\alpha = 1/8(1 - \cos 8\alpha)$.
20. $\tan 2\alpha - \sec \alpha \sin \alpha = \tan \alpha \sec 2\alpha$.

21. $\sin \alpha \cos^3\alpha - \cos \alpha \sin^3\alpha = \frac{1}{4} \sin 4\alpha.$
22. $\cos^4\alpha = (1/8)(3 + 4 \cos 2\alpha + \cos 4\alpha).$
23. $[\cos^2\alpha - \sin^2\alpha]^2 + 4 \sin^2\alpha \cos^2\alpha = 1.$
24. $\sin(\alpha + \beta) \cos(\alpha - \beta) - \cos(\alpha + \beta) \sin(\alpha - \beta) = 2 \sin \beta \cos \beta.$

6. Formulas for Sums and Differences of Sines and Cosines

The following formulas are easily proved. They are frequently useful.

$$\sin A + \sin B = 2 \sin (1/2)(A + B) \cos (1/2)(A - B). \qquad (28)$$
$$\sin A - \sin B = 2 \cos (1/2)(A + B) \sin (1/2)(A - B). \qquad (29)$$
$$\cos A + \cos B = 2 \cos (1/2)(A + B) \cos (1/2)(A - B). \qquad (30)$$
$$\cos A - \cos B = -2 \sin (1/2)(A + B) \sin (1/2)(A - B). \qquad (31)$$

To prove (28) take the formulas for $\sin(\alpha + \beta)$ and $\sin(\alpha - \beta)$ and add. We get:

$$\sin(\alpha + \beta) + \sin(\alpha - \beta) = 2 \sin \alpha \cos \alpha. \qquad (32)$$

Now let

$$\alpha + \beta = A$$
$$\alpha - \beta = B;$$

whereupon $\alpha = (1/2)(A + B)$ and $\beta = (1/2)(A - B)$. Substitute in (32) and we get (28). Formulas (29), (30) and (31) are established in the same way.

EXERCISES

1. Prove formula (29).
2. Prove formula (31).
3. Express $\sin 3\alpha \cos 2\alpha$ in terms of $\sin 5\alpha$ and $\sin\alpha$.
4. Express $\cos 3\alpha \sin 2\alpha$ in terms of $\sin 5\alpha$ and $\sin \alpha$.
5. Express $\cos 2\alpha \cos \alpha$ in terms of $\cos 3\alpha$ and $\cos \alpha$.
6. Write $\sin 5\alpha + \sin 7\alpha$ in terms of $\sin 6\alpha$ and $\cos \alpha$.
7. Write $\sin 5\alpha - \sin 3\alpha$ in terms of $\cos 4\alpha$ and $\sin \alpha$.
8. If $\sin (1/2)(A + B) = 0.7$ and $\cos (1/2)(A - B) = 0.5$, find $\sin A$ and $\sin B$.

7. Some Formulas Re-Proved

The formulas of this chapter can be used to establish in all generality certain formulas already given in Chapter 4 and other formulas. Proofs as given in Chapter 4 usually require several figures. No figures are required here. We prove only a few formulas. The student can elaborate to other formulas if he likes.

$$\sin(180° - \alpha) = \sin 180°\cos \alpha - \cos 180°\sin \alpha$$
$$= 0 \cdot \cos \alpha + 1 \cdot \sin \alpha = \sin \alpha.$$
$$\cos(\tfrac{3}{2}\pi + \alpha) = \cos \tfrac{3}{2}\pi \cos \alpha - \sin \tfrac{3}{2}\pi \sin \alpha$$
$$= 0 \cdot \cos \alpha + 1 \cdot \sin \alpha = \sin \alpha.$$
$$\sin(-\alpha) = \sin(0 - \alpha) = \sin 0 \cos \alpha - \cos 0 \sin \alpha = - \sin \alpha$$
$$\cos(-\alpha) = \cos(0 - \alpha) = \cos 0 \cos \alpha + \sin 0 \sin \alpha = \cos \alpha.$$

EXERCISES

Establish formulas for $\sin(\pi/2 + \alpha)$, $\cos(\pi - \alpha)$, $\tan(\pi/2 - \alpha)$, $\sin(\pi + \alpha)$, $\cos(\pi + \alpha)$.

Chapter 8

The Trigonometric Functions in General

1. Geometric Origin

When we find the area of a square whose side is of length x we multiply x by x. We write this x^2 and read it "x square." However, we know that x^2 has many uses not connected with area. To us it defines a function in which only numbers are involved. We call this an **algebraic function,** in spite of the geometric origin of the name we use so frequently. The ancient Greeks did not use the symbol x^2, but if you were to read their writings you would find them speaking of square numbers; there is little doubt that geometry was in the back of their minds at all times. If we like we can say that x^2 and x^3 have outgrown their geometric origin. Where did the name "x cube" come from? Why do we not have a similar name for x^4?

Now sin x, cos x, and other trigonometric functions also have had a geometric origin. We have seen this. They have many beautiful applications in geometry. We have seen some of these. But as x^2, the trigonometric functions have outgrown their origin. When we write sin x then, x may represent the measure of an angle or it may represent the measure of a time interval or any other thing. In fact x is just a number and sin x just defines a particular function.

2. Definitions and Graphs

The student asks: How do you define sin x if x is not an angle? This matter will be further discussed in Chapter 11. For the present we shall be satisfied with the following definition.

DEFINITION: *Given any real number, x, then* **sin x** *is determined as follows: Consider the angle whose radian measure is x. Determine sin x by the ratio method of Chapter 4. This is by definition the sine of the number x.*

We define the other trigonometric functions in a similar way.

We next desire to draw graphs of the trigonometric functions. Take the Cartesian plane. Let, as usual, x be the abscissa and y the ordinate of a point. We shall consider $y = \sin x$. Given x to find y, we can reduce radian measure to degrees and use an ordinary table of trigonometric functions. However there is an easier method of procedure which is wholly graphical. To save confusion we shall change letters and consider

$$y = \sin \alpha$$

where α is just a number but is also the radian measure of an angle for purposes of our figure. Draw a circle about the origin of unit radius. Let α be the measure of an angle in standard position as indicated in Fig. 30. We now mark 0, $\pi/6$, $\pi/4$, $\pi/3$, $\pi/2$, π, $3/2\,\pi$, 2π, and any other points desired on the x-axis. Construct corresponding angles. Take a pair of dividers and transfer the line segments MP from Fig. 30 to Fig. 31. Sketch a smooth curve through the points at the top of these line segments as indicated in Fig. 31. We know that there is nothing in a particular letter so we replace α by x and have the graph of

$$y = \sin x$$

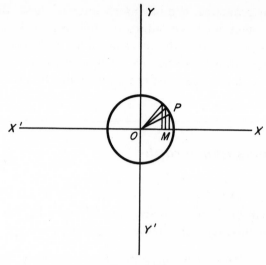

FIGURE 30

as desired. We speak of a *smooth curve*. How do we know that this curve is smooth, whatever that means? As a matter of fact there are many "fine points" about the trigonometric functions, the study of which must be postponed.

We can tell some things from the graph such as

$$\sin 0 = 0$$
$$\sin \pi/2 = 1$$
$$\sin(-x) = -\sin x$$
$$\sin(x + 2\pi) = \sin x$$
$$\sin(\pi - x) = \sin x$$
$$\sin(\pi + x) = -\sin x.$$

We see that sin x increases over the interval $0 \leq x < \pi/2$.

Mention several other things that can be readily recalled by inspecting the figure.

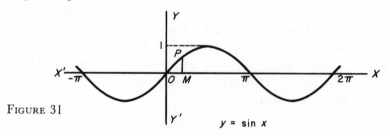

FIGURE 31

$y = \sin x$

3. *Functions Other Than Sin x*

We draw a circle of radius 1 about the origin. Then:

Length OM = cos α,
Length NK = tan α,
Length ST = cot α,
Length OK = sec α,
Length OT = csc α.

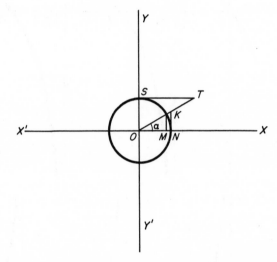

FIGURE 32

The student should carefully verify these statements. We now take a pair of dividers and for various values of α transfer lengths from Fig. 32 to Figs. 33, 34, 35, 36, and 37. We obtain the figures as drawn. Of course these graphs could be arrived at without reference to Fig. 32. However it is doubtful if an easier and more instructive way will be found by the student. We can draw many conclusions

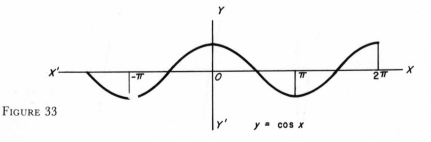

FIGURE 33

y = cos x

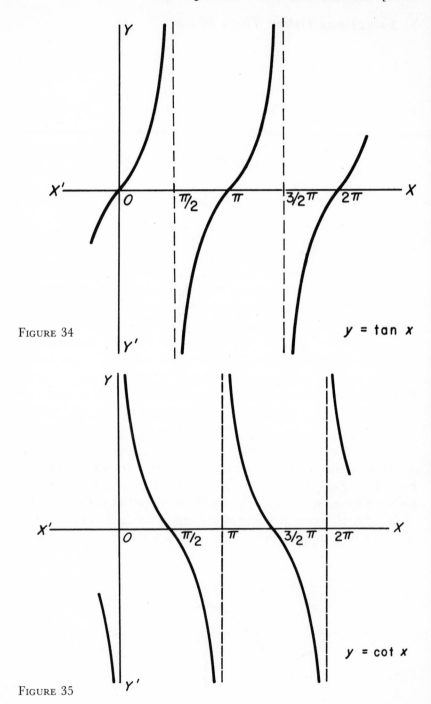

FIGURE 34 $y = \tan x$

FIGURE 35 $y = \cot x$

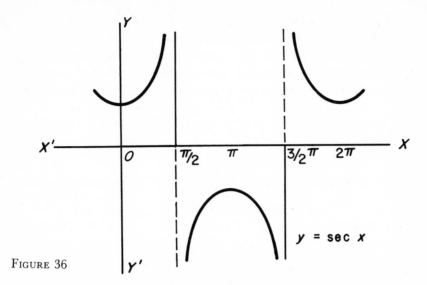

FIGURE 36

$y = \sec x$

from these figures. One of the most interesting is about the behavior of tan x in the neighborhood of $\pi/2$. First, $\pi/2$ is not a permissible value for tan x. However, if x is close to $\pi/2$, yet smaller than $\pi/2$, then tan x is large and positive. It can be made as large as we like by taking x close enough to $\pi/2$. A similar situation exists when x is larger than $\pi/2$ but close to $\pi/2$. Only now tan x is negative.

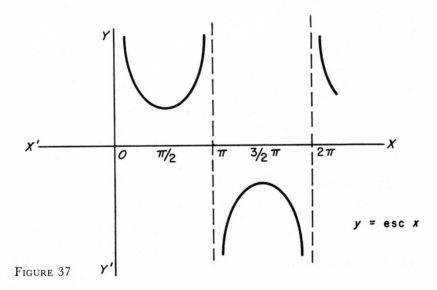

FIGURE 37

$y = \csc x$

There is no motion in mathematical analysis and when we are discussing tan x as a function we are in mathematical analysis. However in describing tan x mathematicians frequently say that *tan x becomes positively infinite* when x approaches $\pi/2$ from below. Similarly tan x becomes negatively infinite when x approaches $\pi/2$ from above. The student will encounter the simple statement "When x approaches $\pi/2$ then tan x becomes infinite." A mathematical shorthand frequently used for this is

$$\lim_{\pi/2} \tan x = \infty.$$

This is not to be construed as meaning in any way that $\pi/2$ (or 90°) has a tangent or that tan x has any limit at $\pi/2$ or that there is any number called infinity. It is simply a convenient technical shorthand.

It now should be clear why the trigonometric functions are frequently called circular functions.

EXERCISES

1. Describe the behavior of cos x when:
(a) $0 \leqq x \leqq \pi/2$; (b) $\pi/2 < x \leqq \pi$; (c) $\pi < x \leqq (3/2)\pi$;
(d) $3/2\pi < x < 2\pi$; (e) $12\pi \leqq x \leqq 12\pi + \pi/2$;
(f) $12\pi + \pi/2 < x \leqq 13\pi$.
2. Discuss sec x when $0 \leqq x \leqq \pi$.
3. Draw graph of $y = \sin 2x$.
4. Draw graph of $y = 2 \sin x$.
5. Draw graph of $y = 2 \sin 2x$.
6. Draw graph of $y = \sin (x + \pi/4)$.
7. Draw graph of $y = 2 \sin(x + \pi/4)$.
8. Draw graph of $y = 2 \sin(x - \pi/4)$.
9. Draw graph of $y = 2 \sin(2x - \pi/4)$.
10. Draw graph of $y = 2 \cos(2x - \pi/4)$.
11. Draw graph of $y = \sin x + 2 \cos x$.

4. Periodicity

DEFINITION: *A function $f(x)$ is called* **periodic** *with* **period** *a if $f(x + a) = f(x)$, $a \neq 0$, for all permissible values of x and if, moreover, whenever x is not permissible, then neither is $x + a$.*

From the definition of the functions

$$\sin(\alpha + 2\pi) = \sin \alpha.$$

Here the measure is in radians. If the measure is in degrees

$$\sin(\alpha + 360°) = \sin \alpha.$$

We consequently see that sin x has the period 2π. Similarly, cos x has the period 2π. We readily show the following theorem

THEOREM: *All the trigonometric functions have the period 2π. In addition tan x and cot x have the period π.*

DEFINITION: *If $f(x)$ has the period $a > 0$ and no smaller positive period, then a is called a* **primitive period** *of $f(x)$.*

EXERCISES

1. Prove that 2π is a primitive period of sin x and of cos x.
2. Prove that if $f(x)$ and $F(x)$ each has the period a and the same domain then $f(x) + F(x)$ has the period a.
3. Prove that if $f(x)$ and $F(x)$ have the period a and the same domain then $f(x) \cdot F(x)$ has the period a.
4. Prove that $2k\pi$ is a period of all the trigonometric functions if $k \neq 0$ is an integer.
5. What is the primitive period of sin kx?
6. What is the primitive period of $\cos(kx + 1)$?
7. Show that π is a primitive period of tan x and of cot x but that it is not a period of sin x or cos x.
8. What is a primitive period of sin $2x \cdot$ sin $3x$? Of sin $2x +$ sin $3x +$ sin $4x$?
9. What is a primitive period of $\sin(1.43)x + \cos(2.71)x$?
10. Is sin $x +$ sin πx periodic?
11. If a and b are two rational numbers, show that sin $ax +$ cos bx is periodic and describe its primitive period.
12. Many natural phenomena are sufficiently close to being periodic to be treated as periodic when studied. One need only mention the magnitude of an ordinary alternating electric current as a function of the time. Mention other physical phenomena that are nearly periodic. Much of the value of the trigonometric functions comes from their use in the study of such phenomena.
13. If a is rational and b irrational, then sin $ax +$ sin bx is an example of what is known as an **almost-periodic** function. Almost-periodic functions have a technical definition not given here. The term *nearly periodic* is frequently used loosely as in problem 12. Give an example of an almost-periodic function by particularizing a and b above. Discuss the function that you give.

Chapter 9

Applications of Trigonometric Functions in Physics

Applications of the trigonometric functions in physics where the independent variable is not an angle are numerous. We proceed to give a few simple examples of such applications.

1. Simple harmonic motion

DEFINITION: *If a particle of matter is attracted toward a point with an attraction equal to a constant a^2 times the distance of the particle from the course of attraction and if the motion is directed along the straight line leading from the particle to the source of attraction and if the particle is subject to no other forces, the motion of the particle is called* **simple harmonic.**

Let y denote the distance of the moving particle from the center of attraction (the source of the attraction) which we shall designate by O. Let t denote the time measured from some agreed instant. Now it is proved in books on mechanics that[1]

$$y = A \sin (at + b) \tag{1}$$

where A and b are constants depending upon the position and velocity of the particle when $t = 0$. Note that $at + b$ is time measured in time units.

We see that $2\pi/a$ is a primitive period of the simple harmonic motion, simply called the **period.** Also, A is called the **amplitude** of the motion and b the **phase.**

For example,

$$y = 2 \sin(3t + 1). \tag{2}$$

Then,

$$\text{amplitude} = 2,$$
$$\text{period} = 2\pi/3;$$
$$\text{phase} = 1.$$

It is proved in books on mechanics that when the position of the particle on its line of motion is given by (1) its velocity is given by

$$v = aA \cos (at + b). \tag{3}$$

units of distance per unit of time.

EXERCISES

Determine the amplitude, period, and phase for each of the simple harmonic motions given in exercises 1 to 4.

1. $y = 4 \sin (5t + \pi/2)$.
2. $y = 3 \sin (t - 1)$.
3. $y = \frac{1}{2} \cos (2t + \frac{1}{2})$.
4. $y = \cos (t - \pi/2.)$.
5. A particle moves subject to the law
$$y = 2 \sin (2t - 1).$$
Find its distance from the center of attraction and its velocity when: **(a)** $t = 0$; **(b)** $t = 1$; **(c)** $t = \frac{1}{4}$.

[1] The student will see at a later time that it is possible to write

$$y = \bar{A} \cos (at - \bar{b}).$$
$$v = -a\bar{A} \sin (at - \bar{b}).$$

He also will see that the names which we use vary somewhat with authors.

6. A particle moves in a straight line subject to an attraction from a point on the line, which attraction is twice the distance of the particle from the center of attraction. The motion is started so that when $t = 0$, then $at + b = \pi/4$ and $y = 2$. Determine a formula for y.

Solution: From the definition of simple harmonic motion $a = \sqrt{2}$. Hence,

$$y = A \sin(\sqrt{2}t + b).$$

When $t = 0$ then $at + b = \pi/4$; hence, $b = \pi/4$.
Moreover, when $t = 0$

$$2 = A \sin(0 + b).$$

Hence,

$$2 = A \sin \frac{\pi}{4}.$$

By the table

$$2 = A(0.707 \cdots).$$

Hence,

$$A = 2.828 \cdots .$$

Consequently,

$$y = 2.828 \sin\left(\sqrt{2}t + \frac{\pi}{4}\right). \qquad \text{Answer.}$$

7. A particle is in simple harmonic motion. Its period is 2π and when $t = 0$ then $y = 3$ and $v = 1$. Find the formula for y.

Solution: $y = A \sin(at + b)$, $v = aA \cos(at + b)$.

But,

$$\frac{2\pi}{a} = 2\pi.$$

Hence,

$$a = 1.$$

Hence,

$$y = A \sin(t + b),$$
$$3 = A \sin b, \qquad (4)$$
$$v = aA \cos(at + b).$$

Hence,

$$1 = A \cos b. \qquad (5)$$

Square (4) and (5) and add and we get:

$$10 = A^2(\cos^2 b + \sin^2 b).$$

But,

$$\cos^2 b + \sin^2 b = 1.$$

Hence,

$$A = \sqrt{10}.$$

Hence, from (4) and (5)

$$\sin b = \frac{3}{\sqrt{10}},$$

$$\cos b = \frac{1}{\sqrt{10}}.$$

We now refer to the table and get

$$b = 1.25.$$

Hence,

$$y = \sqrt{10} \sin(t + 1.25). \qquad \text{Answer.}$$

If n is an integer, the value for b can be varied by $2n\pi$ without numerically affecting the answer.

8. A buoy in the form of an upright cylinder is floating in still water. It is depressed slightly and then released. Show that it will "bob up and down" approximately in simple harmonic motion.

9. Consider the buoy of Exercise 8. Assume the area of the base of the buoy to be 100 square feet and its altitude 2 feet. Assume that the buoy initially floats with its center in the plane of the surface of the water. The buoy is depressed one-half foot and released. Determine a formula for y, the displacement of its center from its initial position. Assume that water weighs 62 pounds per cubic foot.

10. A weight of one pound hangs from the end of a coiled spring. According to Hooke's Law the force is proportional to the elongation of the spring. We assume an elongation of 1 foot when the weight hangs freely but is not disturbed. The weight is now depressed 2 inches and allowed to "bob up and down." Denote the displacement of the weight from its initial position by y. Express y as a function of t.

2. Damped vibrations

Simple harmonic motion is usually only approximated in nature. The motion is slowed down by forces of friction, air resistance, and the like. Such forces are called **damping forces**. It is proved in books on mechanics that in the great majority of such cases a good formula for the displacement is

$$y = Am^{-t} \sin (at + b). \qquad (6)$$

Notice that this formula differs from formula (1) by the presence of m^{-t} where m is a constant.

EXERCISES

1. Given, $m = 2$, $A = 3$, $a = 1$, and $b = 1$, find y by formula (6) when $t = 2$.
2. Given, $m = 3$, $A = 2$, $a = 2$, and $b = 1$, find y by (6) when $t = 1$.

3. Resonance

If simple harmonic motion is subject to an additional impressed force having the same period as the simple harmonic motion, it is proved in books on mechanics that the displacement y is given by the following formula:

$$y = At \sin(at + b). \qquad (7)$$

Notice here the presence of the factor t.

EXERCISES

1. Find y in inches from (7) when $t = 1$ second if $A = 2$ inches, $a = 2$, and $b = 1$ second.
2. Find y in inches from (7) when $t = 2/3$ seconds if $A = 1$ inch, $a = 3$, and $b = 2$ seconds.

4. Electric Currents

The electric current produced by an ordinary alternating electric generator is given by the same formula as is the displacement in simple harmonic motion:

$$i = A \sin(at + b). \qquad (8)$$

EXERCISE

If $A = 10$ amperes and $a = 1$, $b = 1$ second, find the value of i in amperes when $t = 2.5$ seconds.

5. *Motion of a Projectile*

A projectile is fired with a velocity v_0 at an angle α with the horizontal. If the initial point is $(0, 0)$ and if its position at time t is denoted by (x,y), then if there is no air resistance

$$x = v_0 (\cos \alpha)t, \tag{9}$$

$$y = v_0 (\sin \alpha)t - \tfrac{1}{2}gt^2. \tag{10}$$

We shall just assume these formulas. Students who have had a course in physics will find them familiar. The projectile strikes the horizontal plane when $y = 0$ and $t \neq 0$. We immediately find

$$t = \frac{2v_0 \sin \alpha}{g}.$$

Substituting this value in the formula for x and calling the resulting value R we have

$$R = \frac{v_0^2\, 2 \sin \alpha \cos \alpha}{g}.$$

We write this as:

$$R = \frac{v_0^2 \sin 2\alpha}{g}.$$

We call R the range of the projectile. The maximum height is attained when $x = R/2$, that is, when

$$(v_0 \cos \alpha)t = \frac{v_0^2 \sin 2\alpha}{2g}.$$

This yields

$$t = \frac{v_0^2 \sin 2\alpha}{2g\, v_0 \cos \alpha} = \frac{v_0}{g} \sin \alpha.$$

Substitute this in the formula for y and denote the result by M.

EXERCISES

1. Derive a formula for the maximum height of the projectile which we have just studied.

2. Eliminate t between equations (9) and (10). You thus obtain the equation of the path of the projectile in ordinary form. This means a relation between x and y that holds at all points of the path.

3. Show that the maximum range is obtained if $\alpha = 45°$.

4. (a) If $\alpha = 40°$, and $v_0 = 1000$ feet per second, find the range and maximum height.

(b) If $\alpha = 65°$, and $v_0 = 5000$ feet per second, find the range and maximum height.

5. Write the equation of the path of P if $v_0 = v_0$ and (a) $\alpha = 45°$; (b) $\alpha = 60°$; (c) $\alpha = 30°$. Plot these courses.

Chapter 10

Sequences and Series

1. General

A complete understanding of the trigonometric functions can only be achieved when an analytic definition of these functions is given. Analytic definitions can be given in a variety of ways, each of which is equivalent to any other. By an **analytic definition** we mean a definition framed in terms of numbers only and not bringing into play geometric or other concepts. An excellent analytic definition can be given by means of infinite power series. Power series are also of the greatest importance in many other places in mathematics.

This chapter is an introduction to the theory of infinite series. The concepts here are new but no harder than any other new concepts. In particular, sections on geometric progressions and on the binomial theorem are included. They form a good introduction to infinite series and especially to infinite power series. If what is given is already familiar to the student, these sections, of course, can be omitted or better considered a review.

2. *Geometric Progressions*

DEFINITION: *A* **geometric progression** *is a sequence of numbers each one of which, after the first, can be obtained from the preceding one by multiplying it by a fixed number called the common* **ratio.** *The numbers in the progression are called its* **terms.**

We denote the terms by a_1, a_2, a_3, . . . , a_n. We speak of the first term, the second term, the third term, and in general the nth term. We shall denote the common ratio by r.

The following are examples of geometric progressions:

(a)   1, 2, 4, 8, 16, 32, 64;
(b)   1, 1/2, 1/4, 1/8, 1/16, 1/32, 1/64;
(c)   −1, 1/3, −1/9, 1/27, −1/81;
(d)   −1, −1/3, −1/9, −1/27, −1/81;
(e)   0.3, 0.03, 0.003, 0.0003;
(f) $1 + \sqrt{3}$, $4 + 2\sqrt{3}$, $10 + 6\sqrt{3}$.

EXERCISES

1.   What is the common ratio in each of the progressions listed above?
2.   Write down five geometric progressions different from those given in the book. State the value of the common ratio for each of the progressions you have just written down.

3. *The n-th Term of a Geometric Progression*

By the definition of a geometric progression

$$a_2 = ra_1$$
$$a_3 = ra_2 = r^2a_1$$
$$a_4 = ra_3 = r^3a_1$$
$$\text{-----------------}$$
$$\text{-----------------}$$
$$a_n = ra_{n-1} = r^{n-1}a_1. \tag{1}$$

Example: Find the tenth term of the progression: $2, \frac{2}{3}, \frac{2}{9}, \ldots, a_{10}$. By the use of formula (1)

$$a_{10} = 2\left(\frac{1}{3}\right)^9 = \frac{2}{3^9} = \frac{2}{19683}.$$

EXERCISES

1. The first two terms of a geometric progression are $-3, -\frac{3}{2}$. Find the eleventh term.

2. The tenth term of a geometric progression is 100 and the common ratio is $\frac{3}{2}$. Find the third term.

4. *The Sum of a Geometric Progression*

Denote the sum of the first n terms of the geometric progression by s_n.

$$s_n = a_1 + a_2 + a_3 + \cdots + a_n.$$

Substitute for $a_2, a_3, \ldots, a_n$ their values in terms of a_1 and r. We have

$$s_n = a_1 + a_1 r + \cdots + a_1 r^{n-1}. \tag{2}$$

Multiply both sides of this equation by r. We get

$$r s_n = a_1 r + a_1 r^2 + \cdots + a_1 r^n. \tag{3}$$

Subtract (3) from (2) and we get

$$s_n(1 - r) = a_1(1 - r^n).$$

If $1 - r \neq 0$, divide by $(1 - r)$. We get

$$s_n = \frac{a_1(1 - r^n)}{1 - r}, \qquad r \neq 1. \tag{4}$$

If $r = 1$ then:

$$s_n = n a_1. \tag{5}$$

We can write (4) in the form:

$$s_n = \frac{a_1 - a_1 r^n}{1 - r}, \qquad r \neq 1.$$

But:

$$a_n = a_1 r^{n-1}.$$

Hence:

$$s_n = \frac{a_1 - r a_n}{1 - r}, \qquad r \neq 1. \tag{6}$$

Example 1: Find the sum of the numbers

$$1, \, 1/2, \, 1/4, \, 1/8, \, 1/16, \, 1/32, \, 1/64, \, 1/128.$$

Here $n = 8$, $r = 1/2$, $a_1 = 1$.

$$s_8 = \frac{1 - \frac{1}{256}}{1 - \frac{1}{2}} = \frac{\frac{255}{256}}{\frac{1}{2}} = \frac{255}{128}.$$

Example 2: Find the sum of the numbers

$$7, \, 7, \, 7, \, 7, \, 7, \, 7, \, 7.$$

This is a geometric progression with $r = 1$. By formula (5)

$$s_7 = 7 \cdot 7 = 49.$$

EXERCISES

Find a_n and s_n for the geometric progressions given in Exercises 1 to 10.

1. $5, 20, 80, \ldots,$ $(n = 10)$.
2. $-5, 20, -80, \ldots,$ $(n = 10)$.
3. $\frac{1}{3}, \frac{1}{9}, \frac{1}{27}, \ldots,$ $(n = 9)$.
4. $\sqrt{2}, 2, 2\sqrt{2}, \ldots,$ $(n = 14)$.

5. $\dfrac{-3}{\sqrt{2}}, \dfrac{3}{2}, \dfrac{-3}{2\sqrt{2}}, \ldots,$ $(n = 12)$.

6. $\dfrac{1}{\sqrt{5}}, \dfrac{1}{5\sqrt{2}}, \dfrac{1}{10\sqrt{5}}, \ldots,$ $(n = 13)$.

7. $\dfrac{\sqrt{5}}{7}, \sqrt{\dfrac{5}{7}}, \sqrt{5}, \ldots,$ $(n = 10)$.

8. $\dfrac{1}{\sqrt{2}+\sqrt{5}}$, $-\dfrac{1}{3}(\sqrt{2}-\sqrt{5})$, ..., $\quad (n = 100)$.

9. $\sqrt{3}+1, 2, \ldots,$ $\quad (n = 11)$.

10. $\dfrac{2}{\sqrt{3}}$, $\dfrac{2}{3}$, ..., $\quad (n = 9)$.

5. *Infinite Geometric Progressions*

Each student has already met the unending decimal fraction .333 · · · . He is told that the number .33 · · · 3 gets closer to $\frac{1}{3}$ when the number of 3's is increased. This statement is quite correct. Now the fraction 0.3 can be written 3/10, and .33 is just a short way of writing $3/10 + 3/100$. Similarly .333 is $3/10 + 3/100 + 3/1000$, and, in general, .333 · · · 3 can be written $3/10 + 3/100 + 3/1000 + · · · + 3/10^n$. The numbers $3/10, 3/100, \ldots, 3/10^n$ form a geometric progression with common ratio $1/10$. Its sum gets closer and closer to $\frac{1}{3}$ when the number of its terms is increased.

Now as a second example of this kind of thing, suppose that a particle moves from A toward B where the distance from A to B is two. We shall suppose furthermore that the particle goes one-half the distance, namely to C_1, and stops for one second. Now the distance from C_1 to B is 1. Let the particle go one-half of this distance, namely to C_2, and stop one second. The distance of C_2 to B is $\frac{1}{2}$. Let the particle go from C_2 one-half the distance to B, namely $\frac{1}{4}$. Let it now go one-half this remaining distance to B and stop a second at the point which we call C_3. Its total distance from A is now $1 + \frac{1}{2} + \frac{1}{4} + \frac{1}{8}$. Its distance from B is $\frac{1}{8}$. We keep this process up as long as we like, each time letting the particle proceed half of the remaining distance to B and stop a second. Two things are clear:

(1) The particle will never reach B.
(2) We can make it get as close to B as we please by continuing the process long enough. Draw your own figure.

Now, let us consider the general geometric progression. If $S_n = a_1 + a_1 r + a_1 r^2 + · · · + a_1 r^{n-1}$, then we know that

$$S_n = \frac{a_1 - a_1 r^n}{1 - r}, \qquad r \neq 1.$$

If $|r|$ is less than 1, that is if r lies between -1 and 1, then r^n can be made as small as we please by taking n large enough. We express this by saying that r^n has the limit[1] zero. It results that s_n can be made as close to $\dfrac{a}{1-r}$ as we like by taking n large enough. We express this by saying that s_n has the limit $\dfrac{a}{1-r}$. It is not unusual to write $r^n \to 0$, $s_n \to \dfrac{a}{1-r}$. We shall use the letter s for that number which is the limit of s_n:

$$s = \frac{a}{1-r}. \tag{7}$$

DEFINITION: *A geometric progression that has no end is called an* **infinite geometric progression.**

Examples of infinite geometric progressions are 0.3, 0.03, 0.003, $\dots$, $3(0.1)^n$, $\dots$, and 1, $\frac{1}{2}$, $\frac{1}{4}$, $\dots$, $\dfrac{1}{2^{n-1}}$, $\dots$.

DEFINITION: *The* **sequence**[2] *of sums*

$$s_1 = a$$
$$s_2 = a + ar$$
$$s_n = a + ar + ar^2 + \cdots + ar^{n-1}$$
$$\cdots \cdots \cdots \cdots \cdots \cdots \cdots$$

is called an **infinite geometric series.**

We usually simply write

$$a + ar + ar^2 + \cdots + ar^{n-1} + \cdots \tag{8}$$

and call (8) an infinite geometric series.

We refer to a, ar, ar^2, $\dots$, as *terms* of the series.

DEFINITION: *If* $|r| < 1$, *then the number* $s = limit\ s_n$ *is called the* **sum** *of the infinite geometric series.*

[1]The statement " $\dots$ has the limit" means just what the student thinks it does. The ideas involved will be more carefully analyzed in Section 8. For the present we proceed using intuitive ideas only.

[2]This term also means what the student takes it to mean. A precise definition will be given in Section 7.

Notice that s is not a sum in the usual sense, namely, a number gotten by addition. It is a number which is the limit of such a sum. The use of the word "sum" in this new sense is the widening of an already accepted meaning of a word.

In case $a \neq 0$ and $|r|$ is greater than 1 or, equal to 1 then s_n does not have a limit. What is the situation if $a = 0$?

DEFINITION: *In case s_n has a limit the infinite geometric series is said to* **converge** *or to be* **convergent.**

In case s_n does not have a limit the infinite geometric series is said to **diverge** *or to be* **divergent.**

Example 1

$$1 + \frac{1}{3} + \frac{1}{9} + \cdots + \frac{1}{3^{n-1}} + \cdots$$

is convergent since $0 < r = 1/3 < 1$. By formula (7) its sum is $3/2$.

Example 2

$$1 + 1 + 1 + \cdots + 1 + \cdots$$

is divergent, $s_n = n$.

Example 3

$$\frac{5}{4} + \frac{5^2}{4} + \cdots + \frac{5^n}{4} + \cdots$$

is divergent since $r > 1$.

Example 4

$$1 - 1 + 1 - 1 + \cdots + (-1)^{n-1} + \cdots$$

is divergent; $s_n = 0$ if n is even, $s_n = 1$ if n is odd.

6. *Repeating Decimal Fractions*

Repeating decimal fractions can be reduced to ordinary common fractions by means of formula (7). We have already considered .333 · · · · . In the same manner consider .252525 · · · · . Here we have an infinite geometric series with first term .25 and common ratio .01. Hence,

$$s = .252525 \cdots = \frac{.25}{1 - .01} = \frac{25}{99}.$$

If the number has some digits before it begins to repeat the same method can be used:

$$2.41515151 \cdots = 2.4 + \frac{.015}{1 - .01} = 2.4 + \frac{1.5}{99} = \frac{2391}{990}.$$

EXERCISES

Determine which of the infinite geometric series in Exercises 1 to 10 are convergent and which divergent. If the series is convergent determine its sum.

1. $1 - \frac{1}{2} + \frac{1}{4} - \cdots + (-\frac{1}{2})^{n-1} + \cdots$.
2. $3 + 2 + \frac{4}{3} + \cdots + 3(\frac{2}{3})^{n-1} + \cdots$.
3. $-3 + \frac{9}{2} - \frac{27}{4} + \cdots - 3(-\frac{3}{2})^{n-1} + \cdots$.
4. $.777 \cdots$.
5. $.181818 \cdots$.
6. $.232232232 \cdots$.
7. $8 + 4 + 2 + \cdots + 8(\frac{1}{2})^{n-1} + \cdots$.
8. $3 + 3(1 - \sqrt{2}) + 3(1 - \sqrt{2})^2 + \cdots + 3(1 - \sqrt{2})^{n-1} + \cdots$.
9. $4 + 4(\sqrt{3} - \sqrt{2}) + \cdots + 4(\sqrt{3} - \sqrt{2})^{n-1} + \cdots$.
10. $6 + \dfrac{6(\sqrt{3} - \sqrt{2})}{5} + \cdots + \dfrac{6(\sqrt{3} - \sqrt{2})^{n-1}}{5^{n-1}} + \cdots$.
11. $672.3121212 \cdots$.

7. Sequences

The term *sequence* has been freely used in what has gone before. We hope that there has been no confusion We are, however, going to give a technical definition.

DEFINITION: *If when we choose a positive integer n there corresponds to it one and only one number* s_n, *then all the numbers* $s_1, s_2, \ldots, s_n, \ldots$ *constitute an* **infinite sequence,** *or simply a sequence.*

Frequently, a sequence is indicated by $\{s_n\}$. We, however, usually find it unnecessary to write the brace $\{\quad\}$, the context making the meaning clear.[3]

Now s_n may have a limit. This means exactly what the student takes it to mean. We say that s_n has the number s as a limit if the difference between s_n and s is very small in absolute value when n is very large. More precisely, the sequence s_n has s as a **limit** if $|s_n - s|$ is smaller than any positive number we may choose if n is large enough.

Example 1

$$\text{limit } \frac{1}{2^n} = 0.$$

This means that if n is large enough $1/2^n$ which is always positive is as small as we like.

Example 2

$$\text{limit } \frac{n}{n+1} = 1.$$

To show this, we write:

$$\frac{n}{n+1} = \frac{1}{1+1/n}.$$

Now when n is large $1/n$ is small and $1 + 1/n$ is as close to 1 as we wish if n is large enough. This means that $\dfrac{1}{1+1/n}$ is as close to 1 as we wish. In other words limit $\dfrac{n}{n+1} = 1$.

Example 3

$$\text{limit } \frac{2n^2 + 3n + 1}{3n^2 + 4n - 2} = \frac{2}{3}.$$

To show this we write:

$$\frac{2n^2 + 3n + 1}{3n^2 + 4n - 2} = \frac{2 + 3/n + 1/n^2}{3 + 4/n - 2/n^2}.$$

But, $3/n$, $1/n^2$, $4/n$, $2/n^2$ are each as small as desired if n is large enough. We conclude that the fraction is as close to $\frac{2}{3}$ as we like if n is large enough.

[3]For some purposes in mathematics it is convenient to think of the numbers s_n and the numbers n as jointly constituting the sequence. The sequence then appears as a function with domain the positive integers.

EXERCISES

Determine the following limits:
1. limit $1/3^n$.
2. limit$(1 - 1/3^n)$.
3. limit$(\sqrt{n+1} - \sqrt{n})$.
4. limit $\dfrac{2n^3 + 5n^2}{n^3 + n - 1}$.
5. limit $n^{10}/10^n$.

8. Series and Sequences

A formal, precise definition of the limit of a sequence is as follows. Try to understand it. If you find the formal language confusing at first, so does everybody else. We are just saying precisely what we have said already in an informal way.

DEFINITION: *A sequence s_n has the number s as a* **limit** *if given any $\epsilon > 0$ there exists a number N such that whenever $n > N$ then $|s_n - s| < \epsilon$.*

All sequences do not have limits. For example, s_n has no limit if $s_n = n^2$. On the other hand, if $s_n = 1/n$ then s_n has the limit 0.

There are a number of theorems which permit us to tell that a sequence has a limit. One of the most important is the following. We shall state it without proof.

THEOREM I.   *If $s_{n+1} \geq s_n$ and if there exists a number A such that $s_n \leq A$ for all n then s_n has a limit.* Of course, this theorem can be turned around and we have the following.

If $s_{n+1} \leq s_n$ and if $s_n \geq A$ for all n, then s_n has a limit.

In both statements A stands for some particular number. It need not be the same number for two different sequences. Also, if $s_n < A$, then clearly $s_n < A + \delta$ where $\delta > 0$. Consequently, if there is one number A, a second choice could be any number greater than A in the first case, or less than A in the second. Consider $s_n = 1/n$. Here $s_{n+1} < s_n$ and $s_n > 0$. Consequently, s_n has a limit. Also, $s_n > -1$. Consequently, s_n has a limit. This just means that there is more than one choice for A. Mention still another one.

The very useful sequences are those formed from a given sequence now to be described.

Suppose that we have a sequence a_n. We use the letter "a" rather than "s" for reasons that will be apparent immediately. Anyhow, it makes no difference what letter is used.

DEFINITION: *The sums*

$$s_1 = a_1$$
$$s_2 = a_1 + a_2$$
$$s_3 = a_1 + a_2 + a_3$$
$$\cdot \cdot \cdot \cdot \cdot \cdot \cdot \cdot$$
$$s_n = a_1 + a_2 + a_3 + \cdot \cdot \cdot + a_n$$

formed from a sequence a_n form a second sequence which is called an **infinite series** *with respect to the sequence a_n.*

For the infinite series it is customary simply to write

$$a_1 + a_2 + \cdot \cdot \cdot + a_n + \cdot \cdot \cdot \cdot \tag{9}$$

We shall do this.

DEFINITION: *The infinite series (9) is said to* **converge** *if the sequence $s_n = a_1 + a_2 + \cdot \cdot \cdot + a_n$ has a limit.*

DEFINITION: *A series is said to* **diverge** *if it does not converge.*

We frequently use the adjectives "convergent" and "divergent," to describe the series.

DEFINITION: *If s_n has a limit s, then s is called the* **sum** *of the series. The numbers a_n are called the terms of the series. If a_n is written as a formula in n, it is called the* **general term** *of the series.*

Notice that the sum of an infinite series is not a sum in the ordinary sense. We do not get it solely by adding. In some cases we might add the a's for a thousand years and still not get s. According to our definition, s is the limit of a sequence. We write

$$s = a_1 + a_2 + \cdot \cdot \cdot + a_n + \cdot \cdot \cdot \cdot$$

An example of a convergent infinite series is any infinite geometric progression where $|r| < 1$. Here r is the common ratio. Such a series is that which follows.

$$1 + \tfrac{1}{2} + \tfrac{1}{4} + \cdot \cdot \cdot + \tfrac{1}{2}^{n-1} + \cdot \cdot \cdot \cdot \tag{10}$$

Another convergent series is the exponential series[4]

$$1 + 1 + \frac{1}{2!} + \frac{1}{3!} + \cdots + 1/(n-1)! + \cdots. \tag{11}$$

Each term of series (11) after the third is less than the corresponding term of series (10).

An example of a divergent series is any geometric series with $r > 1$, and the first term different from zero. Such series is

$$1 + 2 + 4 + 8 + \cdots + 2^{n-1} + \cdots. \tag{12}$$

Another and more interesting divergent series is the following series.

$$1 + \tfrac{1}{2} + \tfrac{1}{3} + \tfrac{1}{4} + \cdots + 1/n + \cdots. \tag{13}$$

The student is apt to think that this is a convergent series, because its terms decrease, approaching zero. This, however, is not the case. The series is divergent as we shall proceed to show. We insert parentheses as shown below.

$$(1) + (\tfrac{1}{2}) + (\tfrac{1}{3} + \tfrac{1}{4}) + (\tfrac{1}{5} + \tfrac{1}{6} + \tfrac{1}{7} + \tfrac{1}{8}) \tag{14}$$
$$+ (\tfrac{1}{9} + \cdots + \tfrac{1}{16}) + (\tfrac{1}{17} + \cdots + \tfrac{1}{32})$$
$$+ \cdots + (1/(2^{n-1} + 1) + \cdots + 1/2^n) + \cdots.$$

Here

$1 > \tfrac{1}{2};$

$\tfrac{1}{2} = \tfrac{1}{2};$

$(\tfrac{1}{3} + \tfrac{1}{4}) > (\tfrac{1}{4} + \tfrac{1}{4}) = \tfrac{1}{2};$

$(\tfrac{1}{5} + \tfrac{1}{6} + \tfrac{1}{7} + \tfrac{1}{8}) > (\tfrac{1}{8} + \tfrac{1}{8} + \tfrac{1}{8} + \tfrac{1}{8}) = \tfrac{1}{2};$

$(\tfrac{1}{9} + \cdots + \tfrac{1}{16} > \tfrac{1}{2};$

$\cdots \cdots \cdots \cdots \cdots$

$(1/(2^{n-1} + 1) + \cdots + \tfrac{1}{2}^n) > (\tfrac{1}{2}^n + \cdots + \tfrac{1}{2}^n) = 2^{n-1}/2^n = \tfrac{1}{2}.$

Now n denotes the number of terms. Let N be the number of parentheses. Then $s_n > N(\tfrac{1}{2})$, where N is as large as we please if n is large enough. This means that the sum of the first n terms of the series is greater than 100 or 1000 or any number if n is large enough. The series diverges.

Still another interesting example of a divergent series is the following:

$$1 - 1 + 1 - 1 + 1 - \cdots + (-1)^{n-1} + \cdots. \tag{15}$$

[4]For an explanation of the meaning of $(n - 1)!$ see Section 10.

Here s_n alternates between 1 and 0. It does not approach a limit. Hence the series diverges.

Many methods are known for testing series to see if they are convergent or divergent. Unfortunately there is no practicable method which is applicable to all series. However, we do give several very useful theorems.

THEOREM II: *If* $0 < b_n \leqq a_n$ *and if* $a_1 + a_2 + \cdots + a_n + \cdots$ *converges then so does* $b_1 + b_2 + \cdots + b_n + \cdots$.

Proof: Let $\sigma_n = a_1 + a_2 + \cdots + a_n$ and $s_n = b_1 + b_2 + \cdots + b_n$. Let $\sigma = a_1 + a_2 + \cdots + a_n + \cdots$. Then $0 \leqq s_n < \sigma_n < \sigma$; also $s_{n+1} > s_n$. Hence by Theorem I, s_n has a limit. This is the definition of convergence of $b_1 + b_2 + \cdots + b_n + \cdots$.

The following companion theorem is easily proved.

THEOREM III: *If* $0 < a_n \leqq b_n$ *for all* n *and if* $a_1 + a_2 + \cdots + a_n + \cdots$ *diverges, then* $b_1 + b_2 + \cdots + b_n + \cdots$ *diverges also*

The student can easily prove this for himself.

Theorems II and III taken jointly are known as the comparison theorems. The series $a_1 + a_2 + \cdots + a_n + \cdots$ is called the **comparison series.** A useful comparison series is the geometric series. A second very useful comparison series is the following:

$$1 + \frac{1}{2^p} + \frac{1}{2^p} + \cdots + \frac{1}{n^p} + \cdots$$

which we shall call the p-series. The convergence and divergence facts about the p-series are as follows. We shall not prove them.

(a) The p-series converges if $p > 1$.
(b) The p-series diverges if $p \leqq 1$.

Example 1 $\dfrac{1}{2 + 1} + \dfrac{1}{2^2 + 2} + \cdots + \dfrac{1}{2^n + n} + \cdots$

is a convergent series. To show this we need simply remark that each term of the series is less than the corresponding term in the geometric series

$$\frac{1}{2} + \frac{1}{2^2} + \cdots + \frac{1}{2^n} + \cdots$$

which converges since $r = 1/2$.

Terms of the same number are called corresponding. Thus, $\dfrac{1}{2^2}$ and $\dfrac{1}{2^2 + 2}$ are corresponding.

Example 2 $\dfrac{1}{1} + \dfrac{1}{\sqrt{2}} + \dfrac{1}{\sqrt{3}} + \cdots + \dfrac{1}{\sqrt{n}} + \cdots$

is a divergent series since every term is greater than the corresponding term of

$$1 + \frac{1}{2} + \frac{1}{3} + \cdots + \frac{1}{n} + \cdots$$

which we have proved divergent.

Example 3

$$\frac{1}{1 \cdot 2} + \frac{1}{2 \cdot 3} + \frac{1}{3 \cdot 4} + \cdots + \frac{1}{n(n + 1)} + \cdots$$

is convergent. We know this because each term is less than the corresponding term of the p-series

$$\frac{1}{1^2} + \frac{1}{2^2} + \frac{1}{3^2} + \cdots + \frac{1}{n^2} + \cdots$$

which converges because $p > 1$.

Example 4

$$\frac{1}{\sqrt{2} - \sqrt[3]{2}} + \frac{1}{\sqrt{3} - \sqrt[3]{3}} + \cdots + \frac{1}{\sqrt{n} - \sqrt[3]{n}} + \cdots$$

is divergent because

$$\frac{1}{\sqrt{n} - \sqrt[3]{n}} > \frac{1}{\sqrt{n}} = \frac{1}{n^{1/2}}$$

which is the general term of the p series with $p = \frac{1}{2}$ and which is consequently divergent.

EXERCISES

Use the comparison theorem to tell whether each of series 1 and 2 is convergent or divergent.

1. $1 + \dfrac{1}{2 \cdot 2} + \dfrac{1}{3 \cdot 2^2} + \dfrac{1}{4 \cdot 2^3} + \cdots + \dfrac{1}{n \cdot 2^{n-1}} + \cdots$

2. $2 + \dfrac{2}{\sqrt[3]{2}} + \dfrac{2}{\sqrt[3]{3}} + \cdots + \dfrac{2}{\sqrt[3]{n}} + \cdots$

3. By comparison with .999 $\cdots$ prove every unending decimal fraction convergent.

The following theorem which is given without proof, gives a method which is applicable in a great many cases. It frequently is called the **ratio test.**

THEOREM IV: *Given* $a_1 + a_2 + \cdots + a_n + \cdots$. *Suppose* a_{n+1}/a_n *has a limit and let*

$$\text{limit } a_{n+1}/a_n = L.$$

If $|L| < 1$, *then the series converges. If* $|L| > 1$, *then series diverges.*

Example: Determine whether the following series is convergent or divergent.

$$1/2 + 1/2 \cdot 2^2 + 1/3 \cdot 2^3 + \cdots + 1/n \cdot 2^n + \cdots .$$

Here

$$a_n = \frac{1}{n \cdot 2^n}, \ a_{n+1} = \frac{1}{(n + 1)2^{n+1}}.$$

Hence

$$\frac{a_{n+1}}{a_n} = \frac{n2^n}{(n + 1)2^{n+1}} = \frac{n}{n + 1} \cdot \frac{1}{2}.$$

But $\text{limit } \dfrac{n}{n + 1} = 1$. Hence

$$\text{limit } a_{n+1}/a_n = 1/2.$$

That is, $L = \frac{1}{2}$. Hence, the series converges.

EXERCISES

Use Theorem II or Theorem III or Theorem IV to see if the following series are convergent or divergent.[5]

1. $1 + \dfrac{1}{2!} + \dfrac{1}{3!} + \cdots + 1/n! + \cdots .$

[5] For an explanation of the meaning of $n!$ see section 10.

2. $\dfrac{1}{1!} + \dfrac{2}{2!} + \dfrac{3}{3!} + \cdots + \dfrac{n}{n!} + \cdots$.

3. $\frac{1}{4} + \frac{1}{6} + \frac{1}{10} + \cdots + 1/(2^n + 2) + \cdots$.

4. $1 + \frac{1}{2}^2 + \frac{1}{3}^3 + \frac{1}{4}^4 + \cdots + 1/n^n + \cdots$.

5. $10 + 100/1 \cdot 2 + 1000/1 \cdot 2 \cdot 3 + \cdots + 10^n/1 \cdot 2 \cdot 3 \cdots n + \cdots$.

6. $\dfrac{1}{3 + 2 \cdot 3 \cdot 4} + \dfrac{1}{3^2 + 3 \cdot 4 \cdot 5} + \cdots + \dfrac{1}{3^n + (n + 1)(n + 2)(n + 3)} + \cdots$.

7. $\dfrac{2}{1 \cdot 2 \cdot 3} + \dfrac{2^2}{2 \cdot 3 \cdot 4} + \cdots + \dfrac{2^n}{n(n + 1)(n + 2)} + \cdots$.

8. $\dfrac{3}{3} + \dfrac{6}{4} + \cdots + \dfrac{2^n + n}{n + 2} + \cdots$.

9. Series of Functions

It may happen that the terms of an infinite series are functions of a variable. We thus may have a series of the following form:

$$u_1(x) + u_2(x) + \cdots + u_n(x) + \cdots. \tag{16}$$

If we speak of this series as converging when $x = a$ we mean that $u_1(a) + u_2(a) + \cdots + u_n(a) + \cdots$ is convergent.

10. Binomial Theorem

(a) *Factorial notation*

If we write "2" with an exclamation point after it we mean $1 \cdot 2$. Thus $2! = 1 \cdot 2$. If we write "3" with an exclamation point after it we mean $1 \cdot 2 \cdot 3$. Thus $3! = 1 \cdot 2 \cdot 3$.

$$1! = 1$$
$$2! = 1 \cdot 2$$
$$3! = 1 \cdot 2 \cdot 3$$
$$\cdot \quad \cdot \quad \cdot \quad \cdot \quad \cdot$$
$$n! = 1 \cdot 2 \cdot 3 \cdots n, \qquad n > 1$$

Now with this understanding of the meaning of an exclamation point after a number, 0! has no meaning. However, it proves to be convenient to make the following definition.

$$0! = 1.$$

This is a definition; there is nothing to prove. The letter "n" as used above denotes any positive integer. The symbol $n!$ is read **"factorial n,"** sometimes **"n factorial."**

EXERCISES

1. Evaluate $7!$, $9!$, $13!$, $8!$, $12!$.
2. What can you say about the value of $n!$ when n is large?
3. Evaluate $10!/8!$.
4. Evaluate $12!/3! \, 4!$.
5. Write $n!/(n-2)!$ in a different form.
6. Show that $\dfrac{n(n-1)\cdots(n-r+1)}{r!} = \dfrac{n!}{r!(n-r)!}$, $\quad r < n$.

(b)   The formula

Let us multiply $(x + h)$ by $(x + h)$. We obtain

$$(x + h)^2 = x^2 + 2xh + h^2.$$

Similarly, by multiplying $(x + h)$ by $(x + h)$ and then this product by $(x + h)$ we find

$$(x + h)^3 = x^3 + 3x^2h + 3xh^2 + h^3.$$

We then find

$$(x + h)^4 = x^4 + 4x^3h + 6x^2h^2 + 4xh^3 + h^4.$$

We can now find $(x + h)^5$ and then $(x + h)^6$, and so forth. This process soon becomes very tedious and a general formula is imperative. Moreover it develops that in very many places in mathematics, when a theoretical discussion is being made, a formula for $(x + h)^n$ is essential. We shortly shall encounter some such places in this course.

We proved in our algebra course the following formula:

$$(x + h)^n = x^n + nx^{n-1}h + \frac{n(n - 1)}{2!}x^{n-2}h^2 + \cdots + \qquad (17)$$

$$\frac{n(n - 1) \cdots (n - r + 1)}{r!}x^{n-r}h^r + \cdots + h^n.$$

Since

$$\frac{n(n-1) \cdots (n-r+1)}{r!} = \frac{n!}{r!(n-r)!}, \qquad r < n$$

and $0! = 1$ and $a^0 = 1$ provided $a \neq 0$, we can write (17) in the following form if $x \neq 0$, $h \neq 0$.

$$(x+h)^n = \frac{n!}{0! \, n!} x^n h^0 + \frac{n!}{1!(n-1)!} x^{n-1} h + \frac{n!}{2!(n-2)!} x^{n-2} h^2 + \cdots$$

$$+ \frac{n!}{r!(n-r)!} x^{n-r} h^r + \cdots + \frac{n!}{n! \, 0!} x^0 h^n. \qquad (18)$$

EXERCISES

1. Write out $(a+b)^6$ using (17).
2. Write out $(a+b)^6$ using (18).
3. Write out and simplify $(1/x - x)^7$.
4. Write out and simplify $(1/x + x)^7$.
5. Write out and simplify $(1/\sqrt{3} + \sqrt{3})^{10}$.
6. Write out and simplify $(1/y - y)^{10}$.
7. Write out $(a+b)^2$, $(a-b)^2$, $(a+b)^3$, $(a-b)^3$.
8. Write out $(a+b)^4$, $(a-b)^4$, $(a+b)^6$, $(a-b)^6$.
9. What is the tenth term of $(a+b)^{15}$?
10. What is the fifth term of $(x^3 - x^2)^9$?

11. Prove that for any real number $p > 0$ and any positive integer $n > 2$,
$$(1+p)^n > 1 + np + \frac{n(n-1)}{2} p^2.$$

11. Infinite Binomial Series

Suppose we write the following formula:

$$1 + nx + \frac{n(n-1)}{2!} x^2 + \frac{n(n-1)(n-2)}{3!} x^3 + \cdots +$$

$$\frac{n(n-1) \cdots (n-r+1)}{r!} x^r + \cdots. \qquad (19)$$

Here the dotted line at the end means continued indefinitely. Let $n = 2$. Then (19) reduces to

$$1 + 2x + x^2 + 0 + 0 + \cdots = (1 + x)^2.$$

Every term after the third is zero since it contains the factor $(2 - 2) = 0$. Suppose $n = 3$. We get from (19)

$$1 + 3x + 3x^2 + x^3 + 0 + 0 + \cdots = (1 + x)^3.$$

Every term after the fourth is zero since it contains the factor $(3 - 3) = 0$. Let $n = 4$. Series (19) reduces to

$$1 + 4x + 6x^2 + 4x^3 + x^4 + 0 + 0 + \cdots = (1 + x)^4.$$

Every term after the fifth is zero since it contains the factor $(4 - 4) = 0$. In general if $n = r$ (a positive integer) series (19) reduces to

$$1 + rx + \frac{r(r - 1)}{2} x^2 + \cdots + x^r + 0 + 0 + \cdots = (1 + x)^r.$$

Every term after the $(r + 1)$-th is zero.

Now since formula (19) gives $(1 + x)^n$ in case n is a positive integer we naturally ask what about (19) in case n is not a positive integer, say $1/2$? Let us write out what we have in this case. We get the following form:

$$1 + \tfrac{1}{2}x + \frac{\tfrac{1}{2}(\tfrac{1}{2} - 1)}{2!} x^2 + \frac{\tfrac{1}{2}(\tfrac{1}{2} - 1)(\tfrac{1}{2} - 2)}{3!} x^3 + \cdots +$$

$$\frac{\tfrac{1}{2}(\tfrac{1}{2} - 1) \cdots (\tfrac{1}{2} - r + 1)}{r!} x^r + \cdots.$$

This never comes to an end. However, it is a fact that if $-1 < x < 1$ the sum of the first r terms comes as close to $(1 + x)^{1/2} = \sqrt{1 + x}$ as we wish if we simply take r large enough.

In general there is the following theorem.

THEOREM V: *If $|x| < 1$ then*

$$s_r = 1 + nx + \frac{n(n - 1)}{2!} x^2 + \cdots + \frac{n(n - 1) \cdots (n - r + 1)}{r!} x^r$$

can be made as close to $(1 + x)^n$ as we please by taking r large enough.

In other words the infinite series converges. We write

$$(1 + x)^n = 1 + nx + \frac{n(n-1)}{2!} x^2 + \cdots$$

$$+ \frac{n(n-1) \cdots (n-r+1)}{r!} x^r + \cdots$$

This is a hard theorem to prove, and a proof will not be made here.

Example: Approximate[6] $\sqrt{27}$ by the use of (19).

$$\sqrt{27} = \sqrt{25+2} = 5\sqrt{1 + \frac{2}{25}} = 5\left(1 + \frac{2}{25}\right)^{1/2} = 5[1 + \frac{1}{2} \cdot \frac{2}{25} +$$

$$\frac{\frac{1}{2}(\frac{1}{2} - 1)}{2!}\left(\frac{2}{25}\right)^2 + \frac{\frac{1}{2}(\frac{1}{2} - 1)(\frac{1}{2} - 2)}{3!}\left(\frac{2}{25}\right)^3 + \cdots] =$$

$$5[1 + 0.04 - 0.0008 + 0.000032 + \cdots] = 5.196$$

EXERCISES

Find approximate decimal fractions for the following numbers.

1. $\sqrt{29}$ 2. $\sqrt{23}$ 3. $\sqrt[3]{1.3}$
4. $\sqrt[3]{10}$.   5. $\sqrt[6]{70}$ 6. $5^{2/3}$.
7. $(1.1)^{13/14}$ 8. $(\frac{3}{2})^{17/2}$.   9. $(1.1)^{-10}$.
10. $(1.01)^{100}$.   11. $(1.5)^{50}$.   12. $(1.01)^{1000}$.
            13. $(1.1)^{-100}$ 14. $(1.01)^{-1000}$.

12. Power Series in General

DEFINITION: *A series of the type*

$$c_0 + c_1 x + c_2 x^2 + \cdots + c_{n-1} x^{n-1} + \cdots \tag{20}$$

where the c's are constants, is called a **power series** *in x.*

A power series with which we are already familiar is the geometric series:

$$a + ax + ax^2 + \cdots + ax^{n-1} + \cdots$$

also the binomial series given by formula (19).

---

[6]A more detailed discussion of "approximate" and of the use of the equality of sign in expressions such as this is found in Chapter 5.

Some other power series are the following:

(a) $\quad 1 + \dfrac{x}{2} + \dfrac{x^2}{3} + \cdots + \dfrac{x^{n-1}}{n} + \cdots ;$

(b) $\quad 1 - 2x + 3x^2 - 4x^3 + \cdots + (-1)^{n-1}nx^{n-1} + \cdots ;$

(c) $\quad 1 + \dfrac{x}{2^2} + \dfrac{x^2}{3^2} + \cdots + \dfrac{x^{n-1}}{n^2} + \cdots ;$

(d) $\quad 1 - \dfrac{x^2}{2!} + \dfrac{x^4}{4!} - \cdots + (-1)^{n-1} \dfrac{x^{2n-2}}{(2n-2)!} + \cdots ;$

(e) $\quad x - \dfrac{x^3}{3!} + \dfrac{x^5}{5!} - \cdots + (-1)^{n-1} \dfrac{x^{2n-1}}{(2n-1)!} + \cdots .$

In series (d) and (e) certain powers of x are missing. These series will, however, fall under form (20) if the missing terms are supplied with zero coefficients. Thus (d) can be written:

(d') $\quad 1 + 0x - x^2/2! + 0x^3 + x^4/4! - \cdots .$

Each of series (a) to (e), and of others we might write, determines a function of x defined for those values of x for which the series converges.

We state the following theorem without proof.

THEOREM VI: *A power series in x either converges for all values of x or for no values of x other than x = 0, or there exists a number R such that the power series converges when $|x| < R$ and diverges when $|x| > R$.*

If in (20) limit $\dfrac{c_{n+1}}{c_n} = L \neq 0$, then $R = |1/L.|$

If limit $\dfrac{c_{n+1}}{c_n} = 0$ then (20) converges for all values of x.

We call R the **radius of convergence** of the power series. The interval defined by $-R < x < R$ is called the **interval of convergence**. In case the series converges for all values of x we frequently write $R = \infty$.

There are a few rules for working with power series which we must have in our future work. They are natural rules and probably will not be challenged by the student. For convenience of reference these rules are formulated as theorems. Proofs are not given.

Suppose that

$$a_0 + a_1 x + a_2 x^2 + \cdots + a_{n-1} x^{n-1} + \cdots$$

and

$$b_0 + b_1 x + b_2 x^2 + \cdots + b_{n-1} x^{n-1} + \cdots$$

both converge when $|x| < r$. Denote the functions to which they converge by $f_1(x)$ and $f_2(x)$.

$$f_1(x) = a_0 + a_1 x + a_2 x^2 + \cdots + a_{n-1} x^{n-1} + \cdots. \qquad (21)$$

$$f_2(x) = b_0 + b_1 x + b_2 x^2 + \cdots + b_{n-1} x^{n-1} + \cdots. \qquad (22)$$

THEOREM VII:

$f_1(x) + f_2(x) = (a_0 + b_0) + (a_1 + b_1)x + (a_2 + b_2)x^2 + \cdots + (a_{n-1} + b_{n-1})x^{n-1} + \cdots$ when $|x| < r$.

THEOREM VIII:

$f_1(x) - f_2(x) = (a_0 - b_0) + (a_1 - b_1)x + (a_2 - b_2)x^2 + \cdots + (a_{n-1} - b_{n-1})x^{n-1} + \cdots$ when $|x| < r$.

THEOREM IX:

$f_1(x)f_2(x) = (a_0 b_0) + (a_1 b_0 + a_0 b_1)x + (a_2 b_0 + a_1 b_1 + a_0 b_2)x^2 + \cdots + (a_{n-1}b_0 + a_{n-2}b_1 + \cdots + a_1 b_{n-2} + a_0 b_{n-1})x^{n-1} + \cdots$
when $|x| < r$.

THEOREM X: If $f_1(x) = f_2(x)$ when $|x| < r$,   then $a_0 = b_0$, $a_1 = b_1$, $a_2 = b_2$, $\cdots$, $a_{n-1} = b_{n-1}$, $\cdots$.

THEOREM XI: If a power series converges to $f(x)$ when $|x| < r$, then $f(x)$ is a **continuous function** of x when $|x| < r$.

The statement that a function is continuous means exactly what the student thinks it does, namely that a small change in x means a small change in $f(x)$. How small? As small as we like if the change in x is small enough. A rigorous discussion is given in more advanced courses.

Example 1: Find the radius of convergence of $1 + 2x + 3x^2 + \cdots + nx^{n-1} + \cdots$.

$$\frac{c_{n+1}}{c_n} = \frac{n + 1}{n}.$$

But limit $\dfrac{n+1}{n} = 1$. Hence $R = 1$ where R is the radius of con-

vergence. The interval of convergence is $(-1, 1)$.

Example 2: Determine the interval of convergence of

$$1 + \frac{1}{2!} x + \frac{1}{3!} x^2 + \cdots + \frac{1}{n!} x^{n-1} + \cdots .$$

We again apply Theorem VI.

$$\text{Limit } \frac{c_{n+1}}{c_n} = \text{limit } \frac{\dfrac{1}{(n+1)!}}{\dfrac{1}{n!}} = \text{limit } \frac{1}{n+1} = 0.$$

Hence the series converges for all x. The interval of convergence is $(-\infty, \infty)$.

EXERCISES

Find R for each of the following power series. If the series converges for all x we may say that $R = \infty$. If it converges for no value of x other than 0 we say that $R = 0$.

(a) $1 + \dfrac{x}{2} + \dfrac{x^2}{3} + \cdots + \dfrac{x^{n-1}}{n} + \cdots .$

(b) $1 - 2x + 3x^2 - 4x^3 + \cdots + (-1)^{n-1}nx^{n-1} + \cdots .$

(c) $1 + \dfrac{x}{2^2} + \dfrac{x^2}{3^2} + \cdots + \dfrac{x^{n-1}}{n^2} + \cdots .$

(d) $1 - \dfrac{x^2}{2!} + \dfrac{x^4}{4!} - \cdots + (-1)^{n-1}\dfrac{x^{2n-2}}{(2n-2)!} + \cdots .$

(e) $x - \dfrac{x^3}{3!} + \dfrac{x^5}{5!} - \cdots + (-1)^{n-1}\dfrac{x^{2n-1}}{(2n-1)!} + \cdots .$

(f) $1 - \dfrac{x}{2} + \dfrac{x^2}{3} - \cdots + (-1)^{n-1}\dfrac{x^{n-1}}{n} + \cdots .$

(g) $1 + 2x + 2^2x^2 + \cdots + 2^{n-1}x^{n-1} + \cdots .$
(h) $1 + 2!x + 3!x^2 + \cdots + n!x^{n-1} + \cdots .$

(i) $1 + \dfrac{1}{1+2} x + \dfrac{1}{1+2^2} x^2 + \cdots + \dfrac{1}{1+2^{n-1}} x^{n-1} + \cdots .$

Chapter 11

Analytic Trigonometry

1. The Sine and Cosine

Consider the following two infinite power series:

$$\frac{x}{1!} - \frac{x^3}{3!} + \frac{x^5}{5!} + \cdots + (-1)^{n-1}\frac{x^{2n-1}}{(2n-1)!} + \cdots \qquad (1)$$

$$\frac{1}{0!} - \frac{x^2}{2!} + \frac{x^4}{4!} + \cdots + (-1)^{n-1}\frac{x^{2n-2}}{(2n-2)!} + \cdots . \qquad (2)$$

Remember that

$$0! = 1$$
$$1! = 1$$
$$2! = 1 \cdot 2$$
$$\cdots \cdots$$
$$n! = 1 \cdot 2 \cdot 3 \cdots n, \qquad n > 1.$$

We readily prove that series (1) and (2) are convergent for any value of x. We do this by the ratio test of Chapter 10 (Theorem IV).

[1]We could also use Theorem VI.

Consider (1). Here

$$a_n = (-1)^{n-1} \frac{x^{2n-1}}{(2n-1)!}, \quad a_{n+1} = (-1)^n \frac{x^{2n+1}}{(2n+1)!}$$

$$\frac{a_{n+1}}{a_n} = \frac{-x^{2n+1}}{(2n+1)!} \frac{(2n-1)!}{x^{2n-1}} = \frac{-x^2}{2n(2n+1)}.$$

This has the limit zero for any x. Consequently series (1) converges for any value of x. We frequently express this by saying that series (1) converges for all x. We can prove the same thing for series (2) in a precisely similar manner.

Since (1) and (2) converge for all x they serve to define functions of x with domain all numbers. Due to their importance and to the fact that they have been known and studied a long time they are given names. The first is called sine of x, written sin x, and the second is called cosine of x, written cos x.

$$\sin x = x - \frac{x^3}{2!} + \frac{x^5}{5!} + \cdots + (-1)^{n-1} \frac{x^{2n-1}}{(2n-1)!} + \cdots \quad (3)$$

$$\cos x = 1 - \frac{x^2}{2!} + \frac{x^4}{4!} + \cdots + (-1)^{n-1} \frac{x^{2n-2}}{(2n-2)!} + \cdots \quad (4)$$

As a matter of fact, as the student certainly suspects these are the same functions studied in Chapter 8 only defined by another method. We are not prepared to prove this at the present time, so shall proceed as if we had never met the trigonometric functions before. As a matter of fact, the series definitions are in many ways much simpler than the ratio definitions we have heretofore used. They bring in the concept of an infinite series but avoid geometry and the difficult concepts of length and measurement.

2. Approximating Sin x and Cos x

It is far too much trouble to calculate (approximate[2]) values for sin x or cos x every time we need them. Consequently a table is given. See table 2. To show what is involved we shall "calculate" sin $1/2$.

[2]Precise values in terms of recognized symbols of arithmetic are usually impossible to find.

$$\sin \frac{1}{2} = \frac{1}{2} - \frac{1}{3!}\left(\frac{1}{2}\right)^3 + \frac{1}{5!}\left(\frac{1}{2}\right)^5 - \frac{1}{7!}\left(\frac{1}{2}\right)^7 + R$$

where

$$R = \frac{1}{9!}\left(\frac{1}{2}\right)^9 - \frac{1}{11!}\left(\frac{1}{2}\right)^{11} + \frac{1}{13!}\left(\frac{1}{2}\right)^{13} - \frac{1}{15!}\left(\frac{1}{2}\right)^{15} +$$

$$\frac{1}{17!}\left(\frac{1}{2}\right)^{17} + \cdots .$$

By inserting brackets we can write R in the following form

$$R = \left[\frac{1}{9!}\left(\frac{1}{2}\right)^9 - \frac{1}{11!}\left(\frac{1}{2}\right)^{11}\right] + \left[\frac{1}{13!}\left(\frac{1}{2}\right)^{13} -$$

$$\frac{1}{15!}\left(\frac{1}{2}\right)^{15}\right] + \cdots . \tag{5}$$

Also by inserting brackets we write R in the following form:

$$R = \frac{1}{9!}\left(\frac{1}{2}\right)^9 - \left[\frac{1}{11!}\left(\frac{1}{2}\right)^{11} - \frac{1}{13!}\left(\frac{1}{2}\right)^{13}\right] - \tag{6}$$

$$\left[\frac{1}{15!}\left(\frac{1}{2}\right)^{15} - \frac{1}{17!}\left(\frac{1}{2}\right)^{17}\right] - \cdots .$$

Each bracket in (5) is positive and hence R is positive. Each bracket in (6) is positive and hence

$$R < \frac{1}{9!}\left(\frac{1}{2}\right)^9 .$$

Incidentally, we note that the infinite series in (5) and (6) are convergent on account of the convergence of the series for $\sin 1/2$. Let

$$S = \frac{1}{2} - \frac{1}{3!}\left(\frac{1}{2}\right)^3 + \frac{1}{5!}\left(\frac{1}{2}\right)^5 - \frac{1}{7!}\left(\frac{1}{2}\right)^7 .$$

Then

$$\sin \frac{1}{2} = S + R.$$

Simple arithmetic gives the following results.

$$0.500000000 = \frac{1}{2} = 0.500000000$$

$$0.000260416 < \frac{1}{5!}\left(\frac{1}{2}\right)^5 < 0.000260417$$

$$\overline{0.500260416 < \frac{1}{2} + \frac{1}{5!}\left(\frac{1}{2}\right)^5 < 0.500260417.}$$

Moreover,

$$0.020833333 < \frac{1}{3!}\left(\frac{1}{2}\right)^3 < 0.020833334$$

$$0.000001550 < \frac{1}{5!}\left(\frac{1}{2}\right)^5 < 0.000001551.$$

$$\overline{0.020834883 < \frac{1}{3!}\left(\frac{1}{2}\right)^3 + \frac{1}{5!}\left(\frac{1}{2}\right)^5 < 0.020834885.}$$

Hence

$$-0.020834885 < -\frac{1}{3!}\left(\frac{1}{2}\right)^3 - \frac{1}{5!}\left(\frac{1}{2}\right)^5 < -0.020834883.$$

Combining these results we have

$$0.479425531 < S < 0.479425534.$$

Moreover

$$0 < R < \frac{1}{9!}\left(\frac{1}{2}\right)^9 < 0.000000006.$$

Consequently

$$0.479425531 < S + R < 0.479425540.$$

We write

$$\sin \frac{1}{2} = 0.4794255$$

with the statement that it is correct as written to seven decimal places.

The amount of detail here seems great and it could be abbreviated. However, a careful examination of R is necessary in order to be sure that the digits which we give are really correct.

EXERCISES

1. Calculate correct to four decimal places:
    (a) $\cos \frac{1}{2}$;   (b) $\sin \frac{1}{10}$;   (c) $\cos \frac{1}{10}$.
2. Use the value $\sin \frac{1}{2}$ calculated in the text and the values that you have just calculated to calculate:
    (a) $\sin^2 \frac{1}{2} + \cos^2 \frac{1}{2}$;   (b) $\sin^2 \frac{1}{10} + \cos^2 \frac{1}{10}$.
3. Calculate $\dfrac{\sin \frac{1}{2}}{\cos \frac{1}{2}}$ and $\dfrac{1}{\cos \frac{1}{2}}$. Then show that $1 + \left[\dfrac{\sin \frac{1}{2}}{\cos \frac{1}{2}}\right]^2 = \left[\dfrac{1}{\cos \frac{1}{2}}\right]^2$ within

the accuracy of your work.

4. Refer to the tables and find $\sin 1$. Is this twice as great as $\sin 1/2$?
5. Is $\sin 3/2 = \sin 1 + \sin 1/2$?
6. Use tables to verify that within the accuracy of the table

$$\sin^2 0.25 + \cos^2 0.25 = 1.$$

7. What do you guess always to be the value of $\sin^2 x + \cos^2 x$? Do you have a proof of the correctness of your guess?
8. Calculate correct to 5 decimal places:
    (a) $\sin \pi/18$;   (b) $\cos \pi/18$ (assume $\pi = 3.1415927$).

3. *Other Trigonometric Functions*

As you know it is convenient to give names to certain simple and frequently occurring expressions in $\sin x$ and $\cos x$. The following are definitions. There is nothing to prove.

tangent of $x = \sin x/\cos x = \tan x$.
cotangent of $x = \cos x/\sin x = \cot x$.
secant of $x = 1/\cos x = \sec x$.
cosecant of $x = 1/\sin x = \csc x$.

We also remark that in older books on trigonometry sometimes $1 - \cos x$ is called versine of x, written vers x. Similarly $1 - \sin x$ is called coversine of x and is written covers x.

4. *Simpler Identities*

We shall prove that for any x

$$\sin^2 x + \cos^2 x = 1. \tag{7}$$

To do this we multiply the power series defining sin x by itself according to Theorem **IX** of the last chapter. This is exactly as if they were polynomials. We then do the same thing for cos x and add the two resulting series. First

$$\sin^2 x = \frac{x^2}{1!\,1!} - \left(\frac{1}{1!\,3!} + \frac{1}{3!\,1!}\right)x^4 + \left(\frac{1}{1!\,5!} + \frac{1}{3!\,3!} + \frac{1}{5!\,1!}\right)x^6 \qquad (8)$$
$$+ \cdots + (-1)^{n-1}\left(\frac{1}{1!(2n-1)!} + \frac{1}{3!(2n-3)!} + \cdots \right.$$
$$\left. + \frac{1}{(2n-1)!\,1!}\right)x^{2n} + \cdots.$$

In a precisely similar manner we get

$$\cos^2 x = \frac{1}{0!\,0!} - \left(\frac{1}{0!\,2!} + \frac{1}{2!\,0!}\right)x^2 + \left(\frac{1}{0!\,4!} + \frac{1}{2!\,2!} + \frac{1}{4!\,0!}\right)x^4 \qquad (9)$$
$$- \left(\frac{1}{0!\,6!} + \frac{1}{2!\,4!} + \frac{1}{4!\,2!} + \frac{1}{6!\,0!}\right)x^6 + \cdots +$$
$$(-1)^{n-1}\left(\frac{1}{0!\,2n!} + \frac{1}{2!(2n-2)!} + \cdots + \frac{1}{(2n-2)!\,2!}\right.$$
$$\left. + \frac{1}{(2n)!\,0!}\right)x^{2n} + \cdots.$$

Let us add (8) and (9). We get

$$\sin^2 x + \cos^2 x = \frac{1}{0!\,0!} - \frac{1}{2!}\left[\frac{2!}{0!\,2!} - \frac{2!}{1!\,1!} + \frac{2!}{2!\,0!}\right]x^2$$
$$+ \frac{1}{4!}\left[\frac{4!}{0!\,4!} - \frac{4!}{1!\,3!} + \frac{4!}{2!\,2!} - \frac{4!}{3!\,1!} + \frac{4!}{4!\,0!}\right]x^4$$
$$- \frac{1}{6!}\left[\frac{6!}{0!\,6!} - \frac{6!}{1!\,5!} + \frac{6!}{2!\,4!} - \frac{6!}{3!\,3!} + \frac{6!}{4!\,2!}\right.$$
$$\left. - \frac{6!}{5!\,1!} + \frac{6!}{6!\,0!}\right]x^6 + \cdots$$
$$+ \frac{(-1)^n}{(2n)!}\left[\frac{(2n)!}{0!\,2n} - \frac{(2n)!}{1!(2n-1)!} + \cdots \right.$$
$$\left. + \frac{2n!}{(2n)!\,0!}\right]x^{2n} + \cdots.$$

Recall the binomial formula:

$$(1+x)^n = \frac{n!}{0!\,n!} + \frac{n!}{1!(n-1)!}x + \frac{n!}{2!(n-2)!}x^2 + \cdots + \frac{n!}{n!\,0!}x^n$$

and we have

$$\sin^2 x + \cos^2 x = 1 - \frac{1}{2!}(1-1)^2 + \frac{1}{4!}(1-1)^4 - \frac{1}{6!}(1-1)^6 + \cdots$$
$$+ \frac{(-1)^n}{(2n)!}(1-1)^{2n} + \cdots.$$

or $\sin^2 x + \cos^2 x = 1$ which we wished to prove. Formula (7) is one of the basic identities having to do with the trigonometric functions.

If we divide both members of (7) by $\cos^2 x$ we have

$$\sin^2 x / \cos^2 x + 1 = 1/\cos^2 x, \qquad \cos x \neq 0.$$

But $\tan x = \sin x / \cos x$ and $\sec x = 1/\cos x$. Hence

$$\tan^2 x + 1 = \sec^2 x, \qquad \cos x \neq 0.$$

If we divide both sides of (7) by $\sin x$ we obtain

$$1 + \cot^2 x = \csc^2 x, \qquad \sin x \neq 0.$$

Of course, there are results which the student already knows. However, the approach here is new and treats the trigonometric (circular) functions without any reference to geometry.

5. Other Interesting Facts

From (7) we have $\sin^2 x \leq 1$ and $\cos^2 x \leq 1$. Hence

$$|\sin x| \leq 1,$$
$$|\cos x| \leq 1.$$

Consequently,

$$|\sec x| \geq 1,$$
$$|\csc x| \geq 1.$$

From (3), $\sin 0 = 0$. From (4), $\cos 0 = 1$. Moreover

$$\sin x = x\left(1 - \frac{x^2}{3!}\right) + \frac{x^5}{5!}\left(1 - \frac{x^2}{6 \cdot 7}\right) + \cdots$$
$$+ \frac{x^{2n-1}}{(2n-1)!}\left(1 - \frac{x^2}{2n(2n+1)}\right) + \cdots.$$

If $x^2 < 6$ each parenthesis is positive. Hence if $x > 0$ and $x^2 < 6$ then $\sin x$ is positive. Now

$$\cos x = \left(1 - \frac{x^2}{2!}\right) + \frac{x^4}{4!}\left(1 - \frac{x^2}{5 \cdot 6}\right) + \cdots$$

$$+ \frac{x^{2n}}{2n!}\left(1 - \frac{x^2}{(2n+1)(2n+2)}\right) + \cdots .$$

We observe that each parenthesis is positive if $x^2 < 2$. Hence $\cos x$ is positive if x^2 is less than 2.

The series in (3) contains only odd powers of x. Hence

$$\sin(-x) = -\sin x.$$

The series in (4) contains only even powers of x. Hence

$$\cos(-x) = \cos x.$$

If $f(-x) = f(x)$ whenever $f(x)$ is defined, and if when $f(x)$ is not defined $f(-x)$ is not defined, then $f(x)$ is called an *even function*.

If $F(-x) = -F(x)$ whenever $F(x)$ is defined and if when $F(x)$ is not defined $F(-x)$ is not defined, then $F(x)$ is called an *odd function*.

EXERCISES

1. Which of the following is correct whenever the function is defined?
   (a) $\tan(-x) = \tan x$; (b) $\tan(-x) = -\tan x$.
2. Which of the following is correct whenever the function is defined?
   (a) $\sec(-x) = -\sec x$; (b) $\sec(-x) = \sec x$.
3. Which of the following is correct whenever the function is defined?
   (a) $\csc(-x) = -\csc x$; (b) $\csc(-x) = \csc x$.
4. Which of the following is correct whenever the function is defined?
   (a) $\cot(-x) = \cot x$; (b) $\cot(-x) = -\cot x$.
5. Which of the trigonometric functions are odd and which are even?

6. *Definition of Trigonometry*

As has already been inferred the functions of $\sin x$, $\cos x$, $\tan x$, $\cot x$, $\sec x$ and $\csc x$ are called *trigonometric functions*, or *circular functions*.

The study of the trigonometric functions and their applications is called *trigonometry*.

7. *Addition Formulas*

We shall prove the following formula:

$$\sin(x + y) = \sin x \cos y + \cos x \sin y. \tag{10}$$

The proof of this formula is an application of the rule for multiplying two power series together. Remember that this rule simply states that power series can be multiplied together exactly like polynomials. We shall see also that it is necessary to remember the binomial theorem.

$$\sin x = \frac{x}{1!} - \frac{x^3}{3!} + \frac{x^5}{5!} - \cdots + (-1)^{n-1}\frac{x^{2n-1}}{(2n-1)!} + \cdots. \tag{11}$$

$$\cos y = \frac{1}{0!} - \frac{y^2}{2!} + \frac{y^4}{4!} - \cdots + (-1)^{n-1}\frac{y^{2n-2}}{(2n-2)!} + \cdots \tag{12}$$

$$
\begin{aligned}
\sin x \cos y = {} & \frac{x}{1!\,0!} - \frac{x^3}{3!\,0!} + \frac{x^5}{5!\,0!} - \cdots + (-1)^{n-1}\frac{x^{2n-1}}{(2n-1)!\,0!} + \cdots \\[4pt]
& - \frac{xy^2}{1!\,2!} + \frac{x^3y^2}{3!\,2!} - \cdots + (-1)^{n-1}\frac{x^{2n-3}y^2}{(2n-3)!\,2!} + \cdots \\[4pt]
& \quad + \frac{xy^4}{1!\,4!} - \cdots + (-1)^{n-1}\frac{x^{2n-5}y^4}{(2n-5)!\,4!} + \cdots \\[4pt]
& \qquad\qquad \cdots\cdots\cdots\cdots\cdots \\[4pt]
& \qquad\qquad + \frac{(-1)^{n-1}xy^{2n-2}}{1!\,(2n-2)!} + \cdots
\end{aligned}
$$

add by columns and get

$$
\begin{aligned}
\sin x \cos y = {} & \frac{x}{1!\,0!} - \left(\frac{x^3}{3!\,0!} + \frac{xy^2}{1!\,2!}\right) + \left(\frac{x^5}{5!\,0!} + \frac{x^3y^2}{3!\,2!} + \frac{xy^4}{1!\,4!}\right) \\[4pt]
& + \cdots + (-1)^{n-1}\left(\frac{x^{2n-1}}{(2n-1)!\,0!} + \frac{x^{2n-3}y^2}{(2n-3)!\,2!} + \right. \\[4pt]
& \left. \frac{x^{2n-5}y^4}{(2n-5)!\,4!} + \cdots + \frac{xy^{2n-2}}{1!\,(2n-2)!}\right) + \cdots. \tag{13}
\end{aligned}
$$

Now there is nothing peculiar in one letter as against another so far as our purposes are concerned. We consequently interchange letters in (13). We also change the order of terms in each parenthesis. We get

$$\cos x \sin y = \frac{y}{0!\,1!} - \left(\frac{x^2 y}{2!\,1!} + \frac{y^3}{0!\,3!}\right) + \left(\frac{x^4 y}{4!\,1!} + \frac{x^2 y^3}{2!\,3!} + \frac{y^5}{0!\,5!}\right)$$

$$+ \cdots + (-1)^{n-1}\left(\frac{x^{2n-2} y}{(2n-2)!\,1!} + \cdots \right) \qquad (14)$$

$$+ \frac{x^4 y^{2n-5}}{4!\,(2n-5)!} + \frac{x^2 y^{2n-3}}{2!\,(2n-3)!} + \frac{y^{2n-1}}{0!\,(2n-1)!}\right) + \cdots .$$

Let us add (13) and (14). We get

$$\sin x \cos y + \cos x \sin y = \frac{x+y}{0!\,1!} - \frac{1}{3!}\left(\frac{3!}{3!\,0!}x^3 + \frac{3!}{2!\,1!}x^2 y + \frac{3!}{1!\,2!}xy^2 \qquad (15)\right.$$

$$+ \frac{3!}{0!\,3!}y^3\right) + \frac{1}{5!}\left(\frac{5!}{5!\,0!}x^5 + \frac{5!}{4!\,1!}x^4 y + \frac{5!}{3!\,2!}x^3 y^2\right.$$

$$+ \frac{5!}{2!\,3!}x^2 y^3 + \frac{5!}{1!\,4!}xy^4 + \frac{5!}{0!\,5!}y^5\right) + \cdots$$

$$+ \frac{(-1)^{n-1}}{(2n-1)!}\left[\frac{(2n-1)!}{(2n-1)!\,0!}x^{2n-1}\right.$$

$$+ \frac{(2n-1)!}{(2n-2)!\,1!}x^{2n-2}y + \cdots + \frac{(2n-1)!}{0!(2n-1)!}y^{2n-1}\right]$$

$$+ \cdots .$$

We now recall the binomial theorem namely formula (18) of Chapter 10 and we see that we can write (15) as follows:

$$\sin x \cos y + \cos x \sin y = (x+y) - \frac{1}{3!}(x+y)^3 + \frac{1}{5!}(x+y)^5 + \cdots$$

$$+ (-1)^{n-1}\frac{1}{(2n-1)!}(x+y)^{2n-1} + \cdots . \qquad (16)$$

But the righthand member of (16) is precisely $\sin(x+y)$. We consequently have proved what we set out to prove, namely formula (10).

By the method that we have just used, varying details only, we prove the corresponding formula for the cosine.

$$\cos(x+y) = \cos x \cos y - \sin x \sin y. \qquad (17)$$

EXERCISES

1. Using series prove formula (17).
2. Using the formula already derived in this chapter derive formulas for $\sin 2x$, $\sin 3x$, $\sin 4x$.
3. Derive formulas for $\cos 2x$, $\cos 3x$, $\cos 4x$.
4. Derive formulas for $\sin \frac{1}{2}x$, $\cos \frac{1}{2}x$, $\tan \frac{1}{2}x$.
5. Derive formulas for $\sin A - \sin B$, $\cos A - \cos B$, $\sin A + \sin B$, $\cos A + \cos B$.
6. Formulas (7), (10), and (17) are fundamental formulas that involve the trigonometric functions. By their use many other formulas can be proved. The student is advised to review Chapters 6 and 7.

We repeat here a few formulas with which the student is familiar and which we expect shortly to use.

$$\sin 2x = \sin(x + x) = 2 \sin x \cos x.$$
$$\cos 2x = \cos^2 x - \sin^2 x.$$
$$\tan 2x = \frac{2 \tan x}{1 - \tan^2 x}, \qquad 1 - \tan^2 x \neq 0.$$
$$\sin \frac{x}{2} = \pm\sqrt{\frac{1 - \cos x}{2}}.$$
$$\cos \frac{x}{2} = \pm\sqrt{\frac{1 + \cos x}{2}}.$$
$$\tan \frac{x}{2} = \frac{\sin x}{1 + \cos x} = \frac{1 - \cos x}{\sin x}, \qquad \sin x \neq 0.$$

Whether the sign before the radical is plus or minus depends upon the value of $x/2$.

8. Periodicity

From (4) we know that $\cos 0 = 1$. Now $\cos 2$ is negative. To prove this we write:

$$\cos 2 = 1 - \frac{1}{2!}2^2 + \frac{1}{4!}2^4 - \frac{1}{6!}2^6 + \frac{1}{8!}2^8 - \frac{1}{10!}2^{10} + \cdots$$

$$= 1 - \frac{2^2}{2}\left[1 - \frac{1}{3 \cdot 4}2^2\right] - \frac{2^6}{6!}\left[1 - \frac{1}{7 \cdot 8}2^2\right] - \frac{2^{10}}{10!}\left[1 - \frac{1}{11 \cdot 12}2^2\right] + \cdots$$

$$= 1 - \tfrac{4}{3} - \epsilon, \qquad \text{where } \epsilon > 0.$$

Moreover cos x is continuous. Hence it is 0 at at least one point[3]
between 0 and 2. Denote the smallest such value by $\pi/2$. This is a
definition of π. Since $\cos \pi/2 = 0$ and $\sin^2 \pi/2 + \cos^2 \pi/2 = 1$ we
see that $\sin \pi/2 = \pm 1$. But we have already remarked that $\sin x > 0$
when $0 < x < \sqrt{6}$. Consequently,

$$\sin \pi/2 = 1.$$

Now by formulas just given

$$\begin{aligned}
\sin \pi &= \sin 2(\pi/2) = 2 \sin \pi/2 \cos \pi/2 = 0,\\
\cos \pi &= \cos^2 \pi/2 - \sin^2 \pi/2 = -1,\\
\sin 2\pi &= 2 \sin \pi \cos \pi = 0,\\
\cos 2\pi &= \cos^2\pi - \sin^2\pi = 1.
\end{aligned}$$

Moreover

$$\sin(x + 2\pi) = \sin x \cos 2\pi + \cos x \sin 2\pi.$$

Hence

$$\sin(x + 2\pi) = \sin x.$$

We thus prove that $\sin x$ has the period 2π. We next prove that 2π
is the smallest positive period of $\sin x$. Suppose that there were a
smaller positive period. Call it $2c$. Then

$$\sin 2c = \sin(0 + 2c) = \sin 0 = 0,$$

$$\cos 2c = \sin\left(\frac{\pi}{2} + 2c\right) = \sin \frac{\pi}{2} = 1,$$

$$\sin c = \pm\sqrt{\frac{1 - \cos 2c}{2}} = 0,$$

$$\cos c = \pm\sqrt{\frac{1 + \cos 2c}{2}} = \pm 1,$$

Hence $\cos \dfrac{c}{2} = \pm\sqrt{\dfrac{1 + \cos c}{2}} = \pm 1$ or 0. But $0 < c/2 < \pi/2$.
Hence $\cos c/2 \neq 0$.
Hence $\sin c/2 = \pm\sqrt{1 - \cos^2 c/2} = 0$. But $\sin x > 0$ when $0 < x <$
$\sqrt{6}$ and $0 < c/2 < \pi/2 < 2$. In other words $\sin c/2 \neq 0$. This is a
contradiction. Hence 2π is the smallest positive period of $\sin x$. We
call it a **primitive period.** The student is already familiar with this
term.

---

[3]The student will probably not question this. It simply means that if there is no way
around and no bridge or boat or tunnel or plane we can not cross a river without getting
wet.

EXERCISES

1. Prove 2π a primitive period of $\cos x$.
2. Prove π a primitive period of $\tan x$.
3. By the use of your formula find $\sin \pi/4$.
4. Show that $\sin(\pi - x) = \sin x$ but that $\sin(\pi + x) = -\sin x$.
5. Show that $\sin (\pi/2 - x) = \cos x$ and that $\cos (\pi/2 - x) = \sin x$.
6. Show that $\tan \pi/4 = 1$.
7. Derive a formula for $\tan(x - y)$; for $\tan(x + y)$.

9. *Calculus*

When the student has studied calculus he will see that some of the results of this chapter can be obtained with much briefer methods than we have used. For example, from formula (3) the derivative of $\sin x$ is $\cos x$ and from (4) the derivative of $\cos x$ is $-\sin x$. If he differentiates $\sin^2 x + \cos^2 x$, he gets $2 \sin x \cos x - 2 \cdot \cos x \sin x$, which is zero. Consequently, $\sin^2 x + \cos^2 x$ is constant. When $x = 0$ it is 1 and hence it is always 1. Similarly, the formulas for $\sin(x + y)$ and $\cos (x + y)$ are readily obtained by Taylor's formula, and the laborious computation of our chapter is avoided.

The student naturally asks: How do we know that the functions defined by series are the same functions as those arrived at by the ratio definitions? The answer again is calculus. The proof is usually given by what is known as *Maclauren's series*. This is one of the most important formulas in mathematics. The student should look forward to familiarity with it.

Chapter 12

The Exponential and Logarithmic Functions

1. The Exponential Functions

We have seen that power series serve to define functions. Now one of the most important functions is defined by the following power series:

$$1 + x + \frac{x^2}{2!} + \cdots + \frac{x^{n-1}}{(n-1)!} + \cdots. \tag{1}$$

Series (1) converges when x has any value whatever. We can prove this by the use of Theorem IV of Chapter 10. Thus

$$\frac{a_{n+1}}{a_n} = \frac{\dfrac{x^n}{n!}}{\dfrac{x^{n-1}}{(n-1)!}} = \frac{x}{n}$$

Since limit x/n is zero we see that series (1) converges quite regardless of the value of x.

We denote by e^x the function defined by (1). We read this **"e to the x."** We write

$$e^x = 1 + x + \frac{x^2}{2!} + \cdots + \frac{x^{n-1}}{(n-1)!} + \cdots . \tag{2}$$

Since e^x is defined by a power series which converges for all values of x it is a function that is continuous everywhere (Chapter 10, Theorem XI).

Since all signs are positive it follows that if x_1 and x_2 are both positive and $x_1 > x_2$ then $e^{x_1} > e^{x_2}$. We express this by saying that e^x is an *increasing function* when x is positive. We shall see later that e^x is an increasing function of x for all x whether positive, negative or zero.

The function defined by e^x is frequently called the **exponential function.** It is not infrequently written "exp x." Formulas involving e^x may be referred to as *exponential formulas*.

We now proceed to prove a very important theorem about e^x. Unfortunately, it is rather hard to prove.

THEOREM 1.

$$(e^x)\,(e^z) = (e^{x+z}) \tag{3}$$

Proof: We know that power series can be multiplied together precisely as polynomials are multiplied and that the resulting power series will converge for values of the variable lying in an interval within both the intervals of convergence of the power series being multiplied together. We perform the multiplication as follows, grouping together all terms of the same degree.

$$e^x = 1 + x + \frac{x^2}{2!} + \cdots + \frac{x^{n-1}}{(n-1)!} + \cdots$$

$$e^z = 1 + z + \frac{z^2}{2!} + \cdots + \frac{z^{n-1}}{(n-1)!} + \cdots$$

$$(e^x)(e^z) = 1 + (x+z) + \left(\frac{x^2}{2!} + xz + \frac{z^2}{2!}\right) + \left(\frac{x^3}{3!} + \frac{x^2 z}{1!\,2!} + \frac{xz^2}{2!\,1!} + \frac{z^3}{3!}\right)$$

$$+ \cdots + \left(\frac{x^{n-1}}{(n-1)!} + \frac{x^{n-2}z}{(n-2)!\,1!} + \frac{x^{n-3}z^2}{(n-3)!\,2!} + \cdots\right.$$

$$+ \frac{z^{n-1}}{(n-1)!}\Bigg) + \cdots = 1 + (x+z) + \frac{1}{2!}(x^2 + 2xz + z^2)$$

$$+ \frac{1}{3!}\left(x^3 + \frac{3!}{1!\,2!}x^2 z + \frac{3!}{2!\,1!}xz^2 + z^3\right) + \cdots$$

$$+ \frac{1}{(n-1)!}\left(x^{n-1} + \frac{(n-1)!}{(n-2)!\,1!}x^{n-2}z + \frac{(n-1)!}{(n-3)!\,2!}x^{n-3}z^2 + \cdots\right.$$

$$\left. + z^{n-1}\right) + \cdots.$$

We now recall the binomial formula as given in Chapter 10[4]. We then can write

$$e^x e^z = 1 + (x+z) + \frac{1}{2!}(x+z)^2 + \frac{1}{3!}(x+z)^3 + \cdots$$

$$+ \frac{1}{(n-1)!}(x+z)^{n-1} + \cdots,$$

but this is precisely e^{x+z}. We then can write

$$e^x e^z = e^{x+z}$$

proving the theorem.

Formula (3) is one of the basic formulas of all mathematics.

We now define a number which we call "e" as follows:

$$e^1 = e = 1 + 1 + \frac{1}{2!} + \frac{1}{3!} + \cdots + \frac{1}{(n-1)!} + \cdots.$$

By ordinary division we readily establish the following inequalities:

$$1.0000000 = 1 \quad = 1.0000000,$$
$$1.0000000 = 1 \quad = 1.0000000,$$
$$0.5000000 = \frac{1}{2!} = 0.5000000,$$
$$0.1666666 < \frac{1}{3!} < 0.1666667,$$
$$0.0416666 < \frac{1}{4!} < 0.0416667,$$

---

[4]$(x+z)^{n-1} = x^{n-1} + \dfrac{(n-1)!}{(n-2)!\,1!}x^{n-2}z + \dfrac{(n-1)!}{(n-3)!\,2!}x^{n-3}z^2 + \ldots + z^{n-1}.$

$$0.0083333 < \frac{1}{5!} < 0.0083334,$$

$$0.0013888 < \frac{1}{6!} < 0.0013889,$$

$$0.0001984 < \frac{1}{7!} < 0.0001985,$$

$$0.0000248 < \frac{1}{8!} < 0.0000249,$$

$$0.0000027 < \frac{1}{9!} < 0.0000028.$$

Hence by addition

$$2.7182812 < 1 + 1 + \frac{1}{2!} + \cdots + \frac{1}{9!} < 2.7182819. \qquad (4)$$

Now if we write

$$e = 2.71828$$

are we quite sure that we are not really overstating what we know? This can be readily answered. Consider the remaining terms of the series. We denote their sum by R.

$$R = \frac{1}{10!} + \frac{1}{11!} + \frac{1}{12!} + \cdots + \frac{1}{(10+n-1)!} + \cdots < \frac{1}{10!} + \frac{1}{10!} \cdot$$

$$\left(\frac{1}{10}\right) + \frac{1}{10!} \cdot \left(\frac{1}{10}\right)^2 + \cdots + \frac{1}{10!}\left(\frac{1}{10}\right)^{n-1} + \cdots.$$

But this last is a geometric series whose sum is

$$\frac{1}{10!} \cdot \frac{1}{1 - \frac{1}{10}} = \frac{1}{10!} \cdot \frac{10}{9} = \frac{1}{9} \cdot \frac{1}{9!}.$$

Hence

$$0 < R < \frac{1}{9} \cdot \frac{1}{9!} < 0.0000004.$$

Add 0.0000004 to the rightmost member in (4) and we have

$$2.7182812 < e < 2.7182823.$$

Consequently we can write with complete confidence

$$e = 2.71828.$$

Next by (3)

$$e \cdot e = e^1 \cdot e^1 = e^{1+1} = e^2$$
$$e \cdot e \cdot e = (e \cdot e)e = e^3$$
$$\overline{e \cdot e \cdot \cdot \cdot e = e^n}$$

if there are n factors. Moreover let p and q be positive integers.

$$e^{1/q} \cdot e^{1/q} \cdot \cdot \cdot e^{1/q} = e^{1/q + 1/q + \cdot \cdot \cdot + 1/q} = e$$

if there are q factors. That is $e^{1/q}$ is the number which when multiplied by itself $(q - 1)$ times yields e. Thus $e^{1/q}$ is what we have called $\sqrt[q]{e}$. We now know that there is such a number. We did not know this before. Similarly, if there are p factors $e^{1/q} \cdot e^{1/q} \cdot \cdot \cdot e^{1/q} = e^{p/q}$. This is also written $(\sqrt[q]{e})^p$. Moreover if we raise $e^{p/q}$ to the q-th power we have

$$e^{p/q} \cdot e^{p/q} \cdot \cdot \cdot e^{p/q} = e^{p/q + p/q + \cdot \cdot \cdot + p/q} = e^p.$$

This means that $e^{p/q}$ is the q-th root of e^p: $e^{p/q} = \sqrt[q]{e^p}$. Hence

$$(\sqrt[q]{e})^p = \sqrt[q]{e^p}.$$

Moreover

$$e^0 = 1 + 0 + 0 + \cdot \cdot \cdot = 1. \qquad (5)$$

In addition:

$$e^{-x + x} = e^0 = 1$$

Hence

$$e^{-x} = \frac{1}{e^x}. \qquad (6)$$

We thus see that when we write e^x as defined by (2) the x is an exponent as we have understood it in the past so long as x is any *rational number.*

DEFINITION: *A number which can be written in the form p/q where p and q are integers is called a* **rational number.**

Now series (2) has the great advantage of defining e^x for values of x that are not rational. Numbers that are not rational are called *irrational.* Examples of irrational numbers[5] are $\sqrt{2}$, $\sqrt[3]{2}$, π. The student now can tell what is meant by e^π.

[5]It is frequently difficult to prove a given number irrational. Those mentioned and many others, however, have been proved to be irrational.

From equation (6) we conclude that e^x is an increasing function when x is a negative or zero, as well as when x is positive which we have already seen. Remember, for example, that $-4 < -2$; also $e^{-4} = 1/e^4$ is less than $e^{-2} = 1/e^2$ since $e^4 > e^2$. The same reasoning applies to any two negative numbers.

We shall now plot the graph of $y = e^x$, remembering that e^x is a continuous increasing function. We make a table of values.

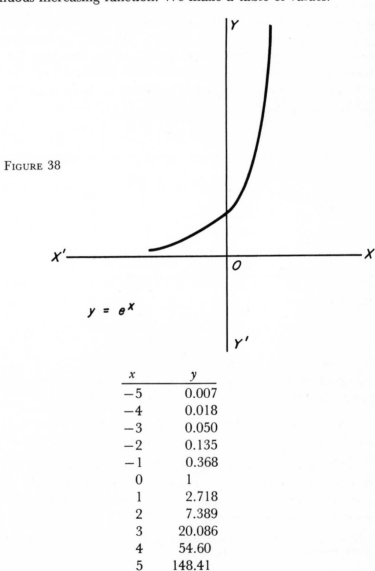

FIGURE 38

$y = e^x$

x	y
-5	0.007
-4	0.018
-3	0.050
-2	0.135
-1	0.368
0	1
1	2.718
2	7.389
3	20.086
4	54.60
5	148.41

For greater values of x, y increases very rapidly becoming perfectly huge very quickly. As a matter of fact it becomes larger than any number that we can mention. Similarly, it approaches zero very rapidly when x is negative and becomes numerically large.

EXERCISES

1. Explain the meaning of e^π.
2. Calculate e^2 correct to four decimal places.
3. Calculate $e^{1/2}$ correct to four decimal places.
4. Calculate $e^{1/10}$ correct to four decimal places. Prove that you have the accuracy that you claim.
5. Calculate e^π correct to two decimal places $(\pi = 3.1415927 \cdots)$.

6. Write as a power of e:

   (a) $\dfrac{e^3 \cdot e^2 \cdot e^5}{e^6}$;

   (b) $\dfrac{e^0 \cdot e^7 \cdot e^8 \cdot e^{-5}}{e^9 \cdot e^{-4} \cdot e^7}$.

7. Write as a power of e:

   (a) $\dfrac{e^2 \cdot e^3 \cdot e^{-6}}{\sqrt{e} \cdot \sqrt[3]{e^4}}$;

   (b) $\dfrac{\sqrt[3]{e^{27}} \cdot \sqrt[4]{e}}{\sqrt{e^9}(\sqrt[5]{e})^{15}}$.

2. Logarithms to the Base e

If

$$a = e^b,$$

then certain names are applied to the three letters that enter the equation. The number e is called the *base*. The number b is called the *exponent* of e. It is also called the logarithm of a to the base e. We thus have two names for b according to which of the numbers a or e we have in mind. To illustrate: I am my mother's son. I am also my sister's brother. I speak of myself as a son, or brother according to the person that I have in mind, mother, sister. Similarly b is exponent if we have e in mind and is logarithm if we have a in mind.

There is nothing to one letter as against another so let us write

$$x = e^y. \tag{7}$$

DEFINITION: *Equation (7) is in every way equivalent to*

$$y = \ln x. \tag{8}$$

We read this: y equals the **logarithm** *of x to the base e.* Some people read it: *y* equals the **natural logarithm** of *x*. Still others read it: *y* equals the **Naperian logarithm** of *x*.

Now when $x = e^y$ then x is a continuous increasing function of *y*. It results that $y = \ln x$ is a continuous increasing function of *x*.

We now wish to draw the graph of $x = e^y$. This is the same as the graph of $y = e^x$, which we have already drawn, with axes interchanged. Refer to Fig. 38 and interchange the letters on the axes.

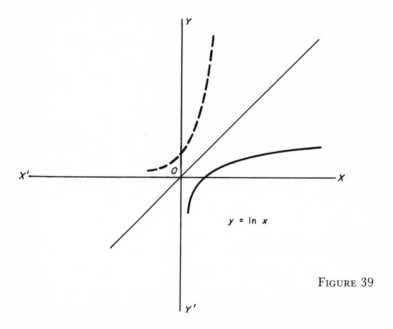

FIGURE 39

Now in order to get the axes in the usual position we rotate the whole figure about the 45° line. We get Fig. 39.

This is the graph of $x = e^y$ or of $y = \ln x$ with the axes in the usual position. We notice that *y is not defined when x is negative*.

Exponential formulas have counterparts as logarithmic formulas. This is true since the logarithmic formula is just the exponential formula written in a different way. The formula

$$e^x e^y = e^{x+y}$$

in logarithmic form is

$$\ln MN = \ln M + \ln N, \qquad M > 0, N > 0. \tag{9}$$

To show this let $e^x = M$ and $e^y = N$. Then $x = \ln M$ and $y = \ln N$. Moreover, since $MN = e^{x+y}$ we have $\ln MN = x + y$. Replace x and y by $\ln M$ and $\ln N$ respectively and we have

$$\ln MN = \ln M + \ln N.$$

In a precisely similar way we can prove

$$\ln\frac{M}{N} = \ln M - \ln N, \qquad M > 0,\ N > 0. \tag{10}$$

We can also establish (10) by the use of (9) as follows: Let $MN = M'$. Then $M = M'/N$. Formula (9) now becomes

$$\ln M' = \ln M'/N + \ln N.$$

Transpose and we have:

$$\ln M'/N = \ln M' - \ln N.$$

We can drop the prime (') since after all M' is any positive number and we have (10). If $M = N$, we have

$$\ln 1 = 0. \tag{11}$$

If $M = 1$, we have:

$$\ln 1/N = -\ln N. \tag{12}$$

Since $(e^x)^p = e^{xp}$ we have:

$$\ln M^p = p \ln M.$$

To prove this let $e^x = M$.

3. *Calculation of Logarithms to the Base e*

Given x to find $\ln x$ is usually something that we can do only approximately and even then it is at best a laborious job.

The following formula is proved in books on calculus.

$$\ln (x + 1) = \ln x + 2\left[\frac{1}{2x + 1} + \frac{1}{3(2x + 1)^3}\right. \tag{13}$$

$$\left. + \frac{1}{5(2x + 1)^5} + \cdots + \frac{1}{(2n - 1)(2x + 1)^{2n-1}} + \cdots \right].$$

The infinite series in the bracket is a power series in $1/(2x + 1)$. It is not hard to show by Theorem IV of Chapter 10 that it converges whenever $|1/(2x + 1)| < 1$. Also $1/(2x + 1)$ is less than 1 whenever x is positive and we are only interested in positive values of x.

Series (13) permits at least the approximate calculation of $\ln (x + 1)$ if $\ln x$ is known. Thus since $\ln 1 = 0$ we can calculate $\ln 2$. Knowing $\ln 2$ we can calculate $\ln 3$. Knowing $\ln 3$ we can calculate $\ln 4$ and so on. Also we know that $\ln 4 = 2 \cdot \ln 2$. So it is not necessary to go back to formula (13) to calculate $\ln 4$. Similarly $\ln 6 = \ln 3 + \ln 2$. However, to get $\ln 5$ or the logarithm of any prime number we go back to (13). (What is a prime number?)

In approximating a number by using the first few terms of an infinite series, and this is what we have meant by the word "calculate," it is always desired to know what accuracy we really have. If we use only the first three terms of the series in brackets in (13) we write

$$\ln (x + 1) = \ln x + 2\left[\frac{1}{2x + 1} + \frac{1}{3(2x + 1)^3} + \frac{1}{5(2x + 1)^5}\right] + R$$

An upper bound for R can be obtained from the formula for the sum of an infinite geometric series, $s = a/(1 - r)$.

$$0 < R < 2\left[\frac{1}{7(2x + 1)^7} + \frac{1}{9(2x + 1)^9} + \frac{1}{11(2x + 1)^{11}} + \cdots\right]$$

$$< \frac{2}{7}\left[\frac{1}{(2x + 1)^7} + \frac{1}{(2x + 1)^9} + \frac{1}{(2x + 1)^{11}} + \cdots\right]$$

$$= \frac{2}{7}\left[\frac{\dfrac{1}{(2x + 1)^7}}{1 - \dfrac{1}{(2x + 1)^2}}\right] = \frac{2}{7}\left[\frac{1}{(2x + 1)^5[(2x + 1)^2 - 1]}\right].$$

This is a convenient formula to use. If more or fewer terms of (13) are used in the calculation precisely similar reasoning leads to a like formula for an upper bound for R.

EXERCISES

1. What is the value of $\ln e$?
2. What is the value of $\ln e^x$?

3. What is the value of $e^{\ln x}$?
4. What is the value of $(\ln e^2)(\ln e^5)$?
5. What is the value of $\exp \ln \exp \frac{1}{2}$?
6. Prove: $\ln PQR = \ln P + \ln Q + \ln R$.
7. Prove $\ln PQ/R = \ln P + \ln Q - \ln R$.

8. Prove $\ln \dfrac{1}{P^m} = -m \ln P$.

9. Prove $\ln \dfrac{PR^m}{\sqrt[n]{Q}} = \ln P + m \ln R - \dfrac{1}{n} \ln Q$.

10. Express as a single logarithm:

    (a) $\ln x + \ln y$;

    (b) $\ln y - \ln x$;

    (c) $2 \ln x - \frac{1}{2} \ln y$;

    (d) $\frac{1}{5} \ln w - 3 \ln z + \frac{4}{5} \ln y$;

    (e) $\frac{1}{2} \ln 7 - \ln 6 - 3 \ln 1$.

    (f) $\frac{1}{5} \ln w - 4 \ln z + \frac{4}{5} \ln y$;

    (g) $\ln 2 - 2 \ln g + g \ln 2$.

11. Solve for y:

    (a) $\ln y = x$;

    (b) $\ln y = x^2$;

    (c) $\ln y = 2 - \ln y^2$;

    (d) $\ln y = 2 + \ln (y + 1)$;

    (e) $\ln (y + 3) = \ln (y^2 + 1) - \ln e^2$.

12. If $\ln i = -\dfrac{RT}{L} + \ln I$, show that $i = I e^{\frac{-RT}{L}}$.

13. If $\ln i = -\dfrac{t}{RC} + \ln \dfrac{E}{R}$, show that $i = E/R\, e^{-t/RC}$.

14. Prove: $\ln 100e - 2 \ln 10 = -\ln e^2 + 3 \ln e$.
15. Prove:

$$\ln \frac{x + \sqrt{x^2 - 1}}{x - \sqrt{x^2 - 1}} = 2 \ln (x + \sqrt{x^2 - 1}).$$

16. Prove:

$$\ln \sqrt{e^2 \sqrt[3]{e^2 \sqrt[5]{e}}} = \frac{41}{30}.$$

17. Calculate $\ln 2$ correct to four decimal places.
18. Calculate $\ln 3$ correct to four decimal places.
19. Calculate $\ln 5$ correct to four decimal places.
20. Calculate $\ln 6$ correct to four decimal places. Check this result by adding $\ln 2$ and $\ln 3$.
21. Calculate $\ln 120$ correct to four decimal places.
22. Calculate $\ln 216$ correct to four decimal places.

4. *The General Exponential*

Let a be any positive number, then let p be the number such that $e^p = a$. There is such a number. It is precisely ln a which we discussed in the last section; $p = \ln a$.

DEFINITION:

$$a^x = e^{(\ln a)x}, \qquad a > 0. \tag{14}$$

This is a definition. There is nothing to prove. It serves to define a^x for all positive values of x. It is read "a to the x" and is known as the **general exponential function.**

From (14) and (6) it follows that

$$a^{-x} = \frac{1}{a^x}.$$

From (14) and (5) it follows that

$$a^0 = 1, \qquad a > 0.$$

It is interesting to note that in case $a = e,$ the definition that we have just given reduces to that already given for e^x. This is highly desirable, in as much as we wish a definition that holds when a is any positive[6] number.

From equations (14) and (3) it follows that

$$a^x \cdot a^y = a^{x+y}.$$

We note in passing that the definition we have given for a^x when x is rational reduces to the definition of elementary algebra. Where we have progressed is that we now have a definition for irrational values of x also.

Inasmuch as $y = a^x$ can be written $y = e^{(\ln a)x}$ we infer immediately that y is a continuous increasing function of x. The graph of $y = 10^x$ is not drawn.

---

[6]The student naturally asks: How do we define a^x if a is negative? The answer is that a satisfactory definition can only be given with the use of imaginary numbers. This is beyond the scope of this book. The student is already familiar with a satisfactory definition when x is a positive or negative integer or zero. This is the definition of elementary algebra. It is $a^n = a \cdot a \cdots a$ to the n factors; $a^{-n} = 1/a^n$; $a^0 = 1$, $a \neq 0$. *We note particularly that 0^0 is not defined.*

EXERCISE

Draw the graph of $y = 10^x$ and of $y = e^x$ with the same set of axes.

5. *The General Logarithm*

DEFINITION: *If*

$$y = a^x$$

we say that x is the **exponent** *of a or the* **logarithm** *of y to the* **base** *a.*

We write

$$x = \log_a y.$$

Of course we can interchange x and y and write

$$y = \log_a x.$$

This means that $x = a^y$. We are more in the habit of writing y as a function of x than of writing x as a function of y.

The most important base, excepting e, is 10. The reason for this will appear in the next chapter where logarithms in computing are discussed.

THEOREM II:

$$ln\ x = (ln\ a)\log_a x \tag{15}$$

Proof: Let $x = a^y$ thus defining y. Then

$$x = e^{(ln\ a)y}.$$

We write this

$$ln\ x = (ln\ a)y$$

But $y = \log_a x$. Hence

$$ln\ x = (ln\ a)\log_a x$$

which is what we were to prove. The reasoning that we have gone through makes no use of particular properties of e. Consequently if a and b are any two positive numbers we have the more general formula.

$$\log_b x = (\log_b a)\log_a x \tag{16}$$

To compute $\log_{10}x$ we compute $\ln x$ and multiply $1/\ln 10$ according to formula (15). We can compute $\ln/10$ by methods of section 3. We find that

$$1/\ln 10 = \log_{10}e.$$

We tell this from (15) by letting $x = e$.

The logarithm to the base 10 obeys the following laws just as does the logarithm to the base e. Independent proof is easy. However, each law is immediately inferred from the corresponding law for logarithms to the base e by multiplying through by $1/\ln 10$. Thus

$$\log_{10}MN = \log_{10}M + \log_{10}N, \tag{17}$$

$$\log_{10}M^m = m\log_{10}M, \tag{18}$$

$$\log_{10}\frac{M}{N} = \log_{10}M - \log_{10}N, \tag{19}$$

$$\log_{10}\frac{1}{N} = -\log_{10}N. \tag{20}$$

The graphs of $y = \log_{10}x$ and $y = \ln x$ should be drawn with the same axes for comparison. These graphs can be gotten from the figure of the exercise by interchanging X and Y and then rotating the whole figure out of its plane about the 45° line as explained in section 2. We note among other things that:

$$\log_{10}1 = 0,$$

that the logarithm is not defined for negative values of x or for zero, that when x gets large y gets large in particular, that $\ln x$ gets large much faster than does $\log_{10}x$. Both curves have the negative y-axis as an asymptote.

Not much discussion has been given to logarithms where the base is other than e or 10. The reason is that these logarithms, as such, are almost never used. If the student wishes to examine the reasoning that we have employed with this in mind he will find that almost every thing said when the base is 10 goes over without change if the base is $b \neq 10$, $b > 1$.

EXERCISES

1. What is the value of:
   (a) $\log_{10}10$;   (b) $\log_{10}1$;   (c) $\log_{10}100$;
   (d) $\log_{10}1000$;   (e) $\log_{10}10^6$;   (f) $\log_{10}0.1$;
   (g) $\log_{10}0.001$.

2. Discuss the behavior of $\log_{10}x$ when x approaches 0.

3. Write as a power of 10:

$$\frac{\sqrt{10}\ \sqrt[3]{10}\ \sqrt[6]{100}\ \sqrt[4]{1000}}{\sqrt{100}\ \sqrt[3]{1000}\ \sqrt[4]{10000}}.$$

4. Compute correct to four decimal places:
   (a) $\log_{10}2$;   (b) $\log_{10}3$;   (c) $\log_{10}6$.

Chapter 13

Computation With the Aid of Logarithms

1. General

In this chapter log x universally means $\log_{10}x$. No other base will be considered.

Formulas (17) to (20) of the last chapter coupled with a table of logarithms are aids in computing that have been used for several hundred years.

Attention is called to the following table.

Exponential Form	Logarithmic Form
$10^3 = 1000$	$\log 1000 = 3$
$10^2 = 100$	$\log 100 = 2$
$10^1 = 10$	$\log 10 = 1$
$10^0 = 1$	$\log 1 = 0$
$10^{-1} = 0.1$	$\log 0.1 = -1$
$10^{-2} = 0.01$	$\log 0.01 = -2$
$10^{-3} = 0.001$	$\log 0.001 = -3$

We know that log x is an increasing function of x. Hence if x lies between 1 and 10 then log x lies between 0 and 1. Under these circumstances it is usual to write log x in the form $0.a_1a_2a_3 \cdots$

$$\log x = 0.a_1a_2a_3 \cdots$$

The decimal fraction part namely $.a_1a_2a_3 \cdots$ is called the **mantissa** of the logarithm. The number to the left of the decimal point, in this case 0, is called the **characteristic** of the logarithm. In general log x is written in decimal form:

$$\log x = a_0.a_1a_2a_3 \cdots.$$

Then a_0 is called the characteristic of the logarithm and $.a_1a_2a_3 \cdots$ the mantissa of the logarithm.

THEOREM I: *The logarithms of two numbers which when written in ordinary decimal form have the same succession of digits have the same mantissas.*

Proof: The proof of this theorem is made by means of formula (17) of chapter 12. Any number not an integral power of 10 is the product of a number between 1 and 10 by an integral power of 10. The number between 1 and 10 determines the mantissa. The power of 10 determines the characteristic.

Theorem I shows us why logarithms to the base 10 are greatly used in computation. One entry in a table will do for all numbers with the same succession of digits quite regardless of the position of the decimal point. For example,

$$234 \qquad = (100)\,(2.34),$$
$$\log 234 \quad = 2 + \log 2.34),$$
$$\log 234 \quad = 2 + 0.3692,$$
$$\log 234 \quad = 2.3692,$$
$$\log 2340 \; = \log(1000)\,(2.34) = 3.3692,$$
$$\log 23400 = \log(10000)\,(2.34) = 4.3692.$$

Again,

$$\log 0.0234 = \log\,(0.01)\,(2.34) \qquad\qquad (1)$$
$$= 0.3692 - 2.$$

It is usual to write a logarithm of this type in the following form:

$$\log 0.0234 = 8.3692 - 10. \qquad\qquad (2)$$

This is obtained from (1) by adding and subtracting 8. We say that the characteristic is -2 or $8 - 10$ according as we refer to (1) or (2). The student must bear in mind that both (1) and (2) give the logarithm as a binomial and that these forms must be handled by the rules of algebra for handling binomials. It is usually most convenient to keep the binomial form. However, occasionally it is convenient to actually perform the subtraction. We have

$$\log 0.0234 = -1.6308.$$

The number $-.6308$ is not what we have called mantissa. A mantissa is the logarithm of a number between 1 and 10 and hence is positive. We can state a rule as follows:

RULE: *If the number is greater than 10 the characteristic of its logarithm is positive and one less than the number of digits to the left of the decimal point. If the number lies between 1 and 10 the characteristic of its logarithm is 0. If the number is less than 1 the characteristic of its logarithm is negative and numerically one greater than the number of zeros to the right of the decimal point before the first nonzero digit is reached.*

Example 1.
Compute N if:

$$N = 2.134 \cdot 3276 \cdot 175.0.$$

Turning to our table we find

$$\begin{aligned}
\log 2.134 &= 0.3292 \\
\log 3276 &= 3.5153 \\
\log 175.0 &= 2.2430 \\
\hline
\log N &= 6.0875 \\
N &= 1223000
\end{aligned}$$

This is the value of N to four figures as given by our table. If the numbers themselves are approximate, errors are probably increased by this multiplication, although the multiplication here is done by means of logarithms. If this is the case, we are only justified in giving 1220000 as answer.

To find the logarithms used in this computation we proceed as follows: To find log 2.134 find 21 in the lefthand column of our table. Look under column headed 3. We find 3284. Under the column headed 4 we find 3304. The difference between these two numbers is 20. The next digit of our number is 4. We take 4/10 of 20 and get 8.

Add this to 3284 and get 3292 which is the desired mantissa. The process just gone through is called interpolation and is to be explained in greater detail in the next section. The characteristic of our logarithm is 0 since the number lies between 1 and 10. To find log 3276, we find log 3.27 = 0.5145 and log 3.28 = 0.5159. The difference between these is 14 in the last two figures. Take 6/10 of this which is approximately 8 and add to the smaller of the two numbers. We obtain 0.5153. The characteristic is 3 since there are four digits in our number to the left of the decimal point. To find the number N which has 6.0875 for its logarithm we search our table for mantissas as close to .0875 as possible. We find that .0875 lies between .0864 and .0899. The first three digits of N are then 122. To find the next digit we proceed in the following way. Find the tabular difference namely .0899 − .0864 = .0035. Now subtract .0864 from .0875. We get .0011. Then form .0011/.0035 = .3 approximately. This is the next digit. There are seven digits to the left of the decimal point in N since the characteristic of log N is 6. We write

$$N = 1223000.$$

This is all right so far as the use of logarithms is concerned. However, as we have remarked, if the original numbers represent measured data or approximate numbers further consideration of errors will probably throw out the final 3 which we have been to so much trouble to work out. Note the 0's at the end of the value which we have worked out for N. In a case like this when we do not know the digits it is customary to write 0's. This is frequently referred to as giving the answer in "round numbers."

Example 2:   Compute N if $N = \dfrac{1.75 \times 2.134}{0.3276}$.

$$\begin{aligned}
\log N &= \log 1.75 + \log 2.134 - \log (0.3276) \\
&= 0.2430 + 0.3292 - (9.5153 - 10) \\
&= 0.2430 + 0.3292 - 9.5153 + 10 = 1.0569 \\
N &= 11.40
\end{aligned}$$

Example 3:   Compute N if $N = \sqrt[7]{125}$.

$$\begin{aligned}
\log 125 &= 2.0969 \\
\log \sqrt[7]{125} &= \tfrac{1}{7}(2.0969) = 0.2996 \\
N &= 1.993
\end{aligned}$$

2. *Interpolation*

We have approximated the logarithms of numbers not to be found directly from the tables by a process known as **interpolation.** This is easily explained by means of the accompanying figure. We assume log x to increase to log $(x + 1)$ along a straight line. This is not the case but gives a close enough approximation for our purposes.

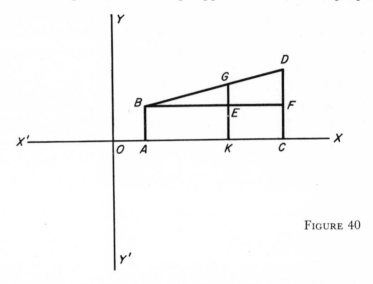

FIGURE 40

Let $OA = x$, $AB = \log x$, $OC = x + 1$, $CD = \log(x + 1)$.
Let OK be the number whose logarithm is wanted.

All right triangles in the figure are similar and since corresponding sides of similar triangles are proportional

$$\frac{EG}{BE} = \frac{FD}{BF}$$

or

$$EG = \frac{BE}{BF} FD = \frac{AK}{AC} FD.$$

We have calculated EG by this formula and added it to AB to get KG which we use for log OK.

Conversely if we are to find OK we find AK and add it to OA. Thus

$$AK = \frac{EG}{FD}AC.$$

The student will observe that in Example 1 of the previous section we performed precisely the operations which have just been explained.

Formulas for the error introduced by interpolation are worked out in more advanced books. *It is found that interpolation in a table of logarithms is accurate to more than the four digits which we have retained.*

EXERCISES

Compute as accurately as your table permits:

1. $10^{1/2}$;

2. $\sqrt[3]{100}$;

3. $\dfrac{(235) \cdot (0.1257)}{623}$;

4. $\dfrac{(0.235) \cdot (125.7)}{6.23}$;

5. $\dfrac{(7632) \cdot (4756)}{321}$;

6. $\dfrac{(11^6) \cdot (7^5) \cdot (2^3)}{(3^2) \cdot (13^4) \cdot (17^2)}$.

The Inverse Trigonometric Functions

1. Multiple-Valued Functions

If we refer to the definition of function in chapter 2 we see that if x is particularized there corresponds one and only one value of y. We now shall denote this type of correspondence, that is the ordered number pairs, by the term **single-valued function.** If, on the other hand, there corresponds to one value of x in general n-values of y, we use the term an **n-valued function.** The words "in general" mean that there may be exceptional values of x to which there correspond less than n values. The number n may be replaced by ∞ and we speak of an infinitely many-valued function. The student, of course, knows that there is no number "infinity." We simply mean that the number of values of y corresponding to a fixed x is greater than any number which we may name in advance.

The name **multiple-valued functions** is used as a heading to this section to cover the situations that we have just described.

2. *Definitions and Graphs*

If we are given the function

$$y = \sin x \qquad (1)$$

defined for all values of x, then x is determined as a function of y so long as

$$-1 \leqq y \leqq 1.$$

However, it is not uniquely determined. We mean by this that when y is given there is more than one value of x which will satisfy equation (1). As a matter of fact there are an infinite number of such values. Thus, if $y = \sqrt{2}/2$, then $\sin x = \sqrt{2}/2$ and $x = \pi/4 + 2n\pi$ or $x = 3\pi/4 + 2n\pi$ where $n = 0, \pm 1, \pm 2, \ldots$ In general, if $y = k$ where $-1 \leq k \leq 1$ and if $\bar{x}$ is so chosen that $k = \sin x$, $-\pi/2 \leq x \leq \pi/2$, then the values of x which satisfy the equation are $x + 2n\pi$ and $\pi - \bar{x} + 2n\pi$, $n = 0 \pm 1, \pm 2, \ldots$ This infinitely multiple valued function is denoted by

$$x = \arcsin y$$

or

$$x = \sin^{-1} y.$$

Both notations have exactly the same meaning. It is particularly to be noted that the " -1 " in the second notation is not an exponent in the usual sense. If we denote the independent variable by x and the dependent variable by y as is usual we have the function

$$y = \arcsin x \qquad (2)$$

or

$$y = \sin^{-1} x. \qquad (3)$$

These are usually read: **"y equals arcsine of x"** or "*y* equals **inverse sine of x"**. Either reading may be given to either notation. Either is entirely equivalent to:

$$\sin y = x.$$

The relationship between $\sin x$ and $\arcsin x$ is the same as that between e^x and $\ln x$ or to that between x^2 and $\pm\sqrt{x}$. In order to draw the graph of $y = \arcsin x$ we first draw the graph of $y = \sin x$. We have already done this. This graph is the graph of $x = \arcsin y$. If we interchange x and y and reletter the figure it is the graph of $y = \arcsin x$ with the $\bar{x}$-axis vertical and $\bar{y}$-axis horizontal. This position of the axes is, however, unusual. To get the axes in the usual position we rotate the figure out of its plane about the line which makes an angle of 45° with the horizontal axis as indicated in the figure.

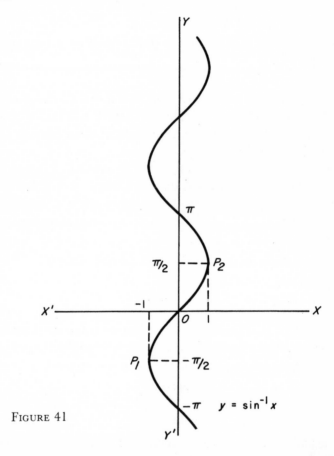

FIGURE 41

It is to be noticed that in the resulting graph (Fig. 41) the curve is very limited in extent along the x-axis. It is, however, unlimited along the y-axis. A parallel to the y-axis cuts it in an infinite number of points. This is what we expect for we remember that arcsin x is infinitely multiple-valued.

Just as we have defined an inverse function to sin x, so we define inverse functions to the other trigonometric functions.

If $x = \cos y$, then
$y = \arccos x$, or
$y = \cos^{-1} x$.

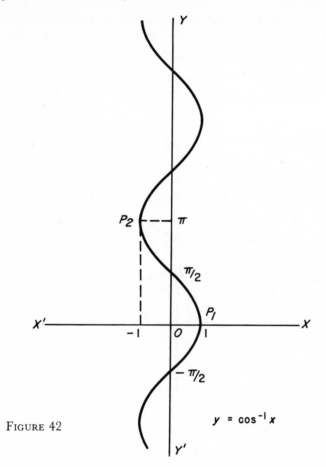

FIGURE 42

If $x = \tan y$, then
  $y = \arctan x$, or
  $y = \tan^{-1} x$.

If $x = \cot y$, then
  $y = \operatorname{arccot} x$, or
  $y = \cot^{-1} x$.

If $x = \sec y$, then
  $y = \operatorname{arcsec} x$, or
  $y = \sec^{-1} x$.

If $x = \csc y$, then
  $y = \operatorname{arccsc} x$, or
  $y = \csc^{-1} x$.

Graphs of $y = \text{arccos } x$ and of $y = \text{arctan } x$ follow. They can be obtained from the graph of $y = \cos x$ and the graph of $y = \tan x$ just as the graph of $y = \text{arcsin } x$ was obtained from that for $y = \sin x$.

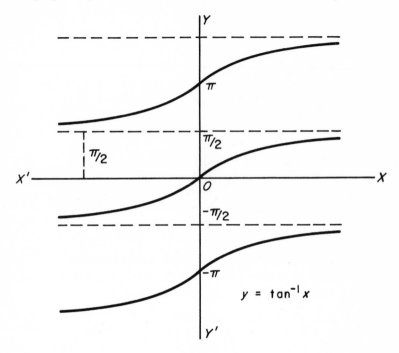

FIGURE 43

3. Principal Values

It is frequently convenient to consider the function corresponding to a portion of the graph of $y = \text{arcsin } x$ as now to be explained. Notice that if in Fig. 41 y is defined by the curve connecting P_1 and P_2, we have a single-valued function. The function thus defined is called the **principal branch** of $y = \text{arcsin } x$. A value for y is called a **principal value.** Here x varies from -1 to 1 and y from $-\pi/2$ to $\pi/2$. Similarly in Fig. 42 the function defined by the curve connecting P_1 and P_2 is called the *principal branch* of $y = \text{arccos } x$. Here x varies from 1 to -1 and y varies from 0 to π. The function defined by the continuous curve passing through the origin in Fig. 43 is called the principal branch of $y = \arctan x$. It is single-valued. Also y is defined for all values of x and varies asymptotically from $-\pi/2$ to $\pi/2$.

Example 1: If $y = \arcsin 1/2$, evaluate y.

$$y = \frac{\pi}{6} + 2n\pi \text{ or } y = \frac{5}{6}\pi + 2n\pi, \qquad n = 0, \pm 1, \pm 2, \cdots.$$

Example 2: If $y = \arctan 0.8423$, evaluate y.

Solution: The principal value for y is taken directly from the table.

$$y = 0.70 + n\pi.$$

Example 3: If $y = \arcsin 3x$, express x as a function of y.

$$x = \tfrac{1}{3} \sin y.$$

Example 4: Prove

$$\arctan \tfrac{1}{4} + \arctan \tfrac{1}{13} = \arctan \tfrac{1}{3},$$

where all inverse functions refer to the principal branch.

Solution: Take the tangent of both sides remembering formula (6) of Chapter 7, also remembering that $\tan(\arctan x) = x$. We get

$$\frac{\tfrac{1}{4} + \tfrac{1}{13}}{1 - \tfrac{1}{4} \cdot \tfrac{1}{13}} = \frac{\tfrac{17}{52}}{\tfrac{51}{52}} = \frac{1}{3}$$

Now if the tangents of two numbers are equal, the numbers differ at most by an integral nultiple of π. Hence

$$\arctan \tfrac{1}{4} + \arctan \tfrac{1}{13} = \arctan \tfrac{1}{3} + n\pi. \tag{4}$$

However, since we are dealing with principal values only, each of the three numbers, $\arctan \tfrac{1}{4}$, $\arctan \tfrac{1}{13}$, and $\arctan \tfrac{1}{3}$ is positive and less than $\dfrac{\pi}{2}$. Consequently if n is numerically as great as 1 we would have the left-hand member of (4) not equal to the right-hand member. It results that $n = 0$ and the equality is established.

EXERCISES

1. Evaluate the following. Use tables if necessary.
   (a) $\arcsin \tfrac{1}{2}$;   (b) $\arccos \tfrac{1}{2}$;

    (**c**)   arctan 1;   (**d**)   arccot 1;

    (**e**)   arcsin 0.0699;   (**f**)   arccos 0.9940;

    (**g**)   arctan 0.2027;   (**h**)   arcsin 0.2474;

    (**i**)   arcsin 0.2592;   (**j**)   arccos 0.3275;

    (**k**)   arctan 1.245.

2. Evaluate the following:

    (**a**)   sin arcsin 0.7;   (**b**)   tan arctan $\frac{1}{2}$;

    (**c**)   arcsin sin $\pi/6$;   (**d**)   arctan tan $\pi/4$.

3. Given $y = $ arccos $\frac{1}{2}$ + arctan 1; without tables find sin y, cos y. Consider principal values only.

4. Given $y = $ arccos $\frac{1}{3}$ + arcsin $\frac{1}{3}$; without tables find y. Consider principal values only.

5. Given $y = 2$ arcsin $\frac{1}{2}$ − arccos $\frac{1}{3}$; without tables find sin y.

6. Given $y = \frac{1}{2}$ arccos 0.6 + arcsin 0.4; find cos y.

7. Show, that when dealing with principal values:

$$\text{arcsin } \tfrac{3}{5} + \text{arcsin } \tfrac{5}{13} = \text{arctan } \tfrac{56}{33}.$$

8. Show that there are determinations of the functions such that:

$$\tfrac{5}{4}\pi = 4 \text{ arctan } \tfrac{1}{5} - \text{arctan } \tfrac{1}{239}.$$

9. Show that there is a determination of the functions such that:

$$\text{arcsin } \tfrac{4}{5} + \text{arcsin } \tfrac{5}{13} + \text{arcsin } \tfrac{15}{25} = \text{arcsin } \tfrac{12}{13}.$$

10. Draw graphs of the following functions from memory.

    (**a**) $y = $ arcsin x;   (**b**) $y = $ arccos x;

    (**c**) $y = $ arctan x;   (**d**) $y = $ arccot x.

11. Explain in detail what is meant by a multiple-valued function.

12. Discuss the variation of the principal branch of arcsin x as x varies from -1 to 1.

13. Does it make sense to speak of arcsin 2?

14. Does it make sense to speak of arccos (-2)?

4. *Inverse Functions as Angles*

It has been pointed out many times that in that part of elementary trigonometry which has to do with the solution of triangles the trigonometric functions are thought of as functions of an angle, or better, of the measure of an angle and that the angle may be measured with any unit, for example the degree. In this part of trigonometry $\sin^{-1}x$ is sometimes read, "the angle whose sine is x." Similarly arcsin x is frequently read, "the angle whose sine is x." Each of the other inverse functions is read in a similar manner.

Example 1: If $y = \arcsin \sqrt{3}/2$, what is y in degrees?

$$y = 60° + n360° \text{ or } 120° + n360°.$$

Example 2: If $y = \sin^{-1}\frac{1}{2}$, what is y in radians?

$$y = \frac{\pi}{6} + 2n\pi \text{ radians}$$

or

$$y = \frac{5}{6}\pi + 2n\pi \text{ radians}.$$

EXERCISES

1. Find the following angles in degrees. Use tables.
   (a) arcsin 0.3214; (b) arccos 0.7621;
   (c) $\tan^{-1}1.423$; (d) $\sin^{-1}0.7315$;
   (e) $\cos^{-1}0.1128$; (f) $\sin^{-1}0.1763$.
2. Find the following angles in radians.
   (a) $\tan^{-1}0.2345$; (b) arcsin 0.6314;
   (c) $\cos^{-1}0.8669$.
3. Find the following angles in mils.
   (a) $\tan^{-1}0.0123$; (b) arctan 0.1234;
   (c) $\sin^{-1}0.3215$; (d) arccos 0.8763.
4. (a) What is sin arcsin x?
   (b) What is arcsin sin $a°$
5. Evaluate:
   (a) $\cos \sin^{-1} \frac{3}{5}$; (b) $\tan \cot^{-1}4$.
6. Evaluate in degrees.
   (a) arccos sin 43°; (b) arctan cot 75°.
7. Evaluate in radians.
   (a) arccos sin $\pi/6$; (b) arcsin cos $\pi/4$;
   (c) arctan sin $\pi/3$; (d) arcsin tan $\pi/6$.

Trigonometric Equations

Certain trigonometric equations can be solved by methods now at the disposal of the student. The kind of thing involved will be illustrated by a few examples. The whole matter is one where ingenuity and numerical skill play a major role.

Example 1.

$$100 \sin^2 x - 110 \sin x + 30 = 0. \tag{1}$$

Find x.

Solution: Equation (1) is a quadratic equation in $\sin x$. We solve for $\sin x$. The easiest way is by factoring (1). We get

$$(10 \sin x - 5)(10 \sin x - 6) = 0. \tag{2}$$

We equate each factor to 0 separately. First

$$10 \sin x - 5 = 0$$
$$\sin x = \tfrac{1}{2}$$
$$x = \pi/6 + 2n\pi, \text{ or } 5\pi/6 + 2n\pi.$$

These values do satisfy (1).
Second

$$10 \sin x - 6 = 0$$
$$\sin x = 0.6$$
$$x = 0.643 + 2n\pi \tag{3}$$

and

$$x = (\pi - 0.643) + 2n\pi.$$

The value 0.643 is obtained from a table of sines. The values given in (3) also satisfy (1) within the limits of accuracy of the table.

Example 2.

$$\sin x + \cos x = 1. \tag{4}$$

Find x.

Solution: *Method 1.*
From (4) we must have:

$$\cos x = 1 - \sin x,$$
$$\cos^2 x = 1 - 2 \sin x + \sin^2 x.$$

But for any x

$$\cos^2 x = 1 - \sin^2 x.$$

Hence

$$1 - \sin^2 x = 1 - 2 \sin x + \sin^2 x.$$

Transposing and dividing through by 2

$$\sin^2 x - \sin x = 0.$$

Hence, if our equation has a solution either

$$\sin x = 0$$

or

$$\sin x = 1.$$

If $\sin x = 0$,

$$x = 0 + n\pi.$$

If $\sin x = 1$,

$$x = \pi/2 + 2n\pi.$$

It is readily found by substitution that $x = 0 + n\pi$ satisfies the equation only if n is even but $\pi/2 + 2n\pi$ satisfies the equation for all values of n.

Method 2.

Divide both members of (4) by $\sqrt{2}$. We get

$$(1/\sqrt{2}) \sin x + (1/\sqrt{2}) \cos x = 1/\sqrt{2}.$$

But $\sin \pi/4 = 1/\sqrt{2}$, and $\cos \pi/4 = 1/\sqrt{2}$.

Consequently,

$$\sin x \cos \pi/4 + \cos x \sin \pi/4 = \sin \pi/4.$$

Hence

$$\sin (x + \pi/4) = \sin \pi/4.$$

Hence, if our equation has a solution

$$x + \pi/4 = \pi/4 + 2n\pi \text{ or } \tfrac{3}{4}\pi + 2n\pi.$$

Hence, $x = 0 + 2n\pi$ or $\pi/2 + 2n\pi$ as above.

Example 3.

$$4 \sin x - 3 \cos x = 2. \tag{5}$$

Find x.

Solution: Divide both sides of this equation by $\sqrt{4^2 + 3^2}$. We get

$$\tfrac{4}{5} \sin x - \tfrac{3}{5} \cos x = \tfrac{2}{5}.$$

Choose y so that $\sin y = \tfrac{3}{5}$, $\cos y = \tfrac{4}{5}$. From our table we find $y = 0.643$. Moreover $\sin 0.411 = \tfrac{2}{5}$.

Consequently,

$$\sin (x - 0.643) = \sin 0.411.$$

Hence

$$x - 0.643 = 0.411 + 2n\pi$$

or

$$x - 0.643 = \pi - 0.411 + 2n\pi.$$

Consequently, we must have

$$x = 1.054 + 2n\pi$$

or

$$x = \pi - 0.232 + 2n.$$

Trial shows that these values which have been obtained as necessary forms approximately satisfy the equation.

Equation (5) could also be solved by substituting $\sqrt{1 - \sin^2 x}$ for $\cos x$ or $\sqrt{1 - \cos^2 x}$ for $\sin x$.

Example 4.

$$\tfrac{1}{2}x - \sin x = 0.$$

Find x.

Solution: An approximate answer to this problem can be found by replacing $\sin x$ by the first two terms of its series definition. Thus

$$\tfrac{1}{2}x - \left(x - \frac{x^3}{3!}\right) = 0.$$

This reduces to:

$$x\left(-\frac{1}{2} + \frac{x^2}{6}\right) = 0.$$

From this $x = 0$, $x = \pm\sqrt{3} = \pm 1.73$. The value $x = 0$ is precise. It clearly satisfies the equation. We can roughly check the value 1.73 from our table. We find that it is too small. Successive trials show that 1.88 is a better value. A graph shows that if x is a solution so is $-x$.

The careful drawing of graphs give results that are accurate enough for many purposes. To illustrate we wish values of x for which $\tfrac{1}{2}x = \sin x$. We carefully draw graphs of $y = \tfrac{1}{2}x$ and of $y = \sin x$. We then measure as carefully as we can the abscissas of the points where the two graphs cross.

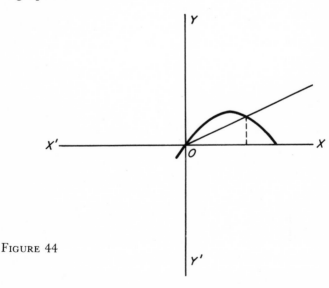

FIGURE 44

Methods for obtaining more and more accurate approximations for solutions of equations such as the one with which we are dealing should be discussed later in the student's mathematical career.

EXERCISES

Solve the following equations or show that no solution is possible.

1. $\sin 2x + \cos x = 0$ 2. $(\cos^2 x)(4\cos^2 x - 1) = 0$
3. $2\csc^2 x - 5\cot x + 1 = 0$ 4. $2\cos^2 2x + \sin 2x - 1 = 0$
5. $2\sin 2x + \cos 2x - 1 = 0$ 6. $(\cos \frac{1}{2}x)(2\sin 4x - 1) = 0$
7. $\tan^2 x = \sin 2x$ 8. $\sin x + 3\cos x = 1$
9. $2\sin x - 3\cos x = 2$ 10. $2\sin x + \cos x = 1$
11. $\sin x = x - 1$ 12. $\tan x = 1 - x$
13. $\cos x = x^2$ 14. $x = 2 + \sin x$
15. $\sin x + \cos x = 1.5$

Chapter 16

Solution of Oblique Triangles Without the Use of Logarithms

1. Fundamental Ideas

A triangle has six parts, three sides and three angles. If we are given the measure of three parts, at least one of which is a side, we can find possible measures of the other three parts. This is what is known as **solving** the triangle.

In this chapter we are interested only in the measure of the parts of a triangle. As a consequence, *triangles which are congruent are considered the same triangle.*

A triangle is said to be **determined** when the measures of three parts are given, if there exists a triangle having parts with the given measures, and if the measures of all the other parts can be determined uniquely by means of the given measures.

When we refer to a part of a triangle we usually refer to the measure of the part. It will be clear from the context when this is not the case.

It is immediate that the three angles do not serve to determine a triangle. However, a triangle is determined in each of the following three cases:

I. Given two angles and the side included between them provided that the sum of the angles is less than 180°.

II. Given two sides and the angle included by them provided that the angle is less than 180°.

III. Given the three sides provided that no side is as great as the sum of the other two sides.

IV. A triangle is sometimes determined if we are given two sides and the angle opposite one of them. It may be that no triangle can exist with the given parts. It also may be that either of two different triangles contain the given parts or finally there may be just one triangle that contains the given parts. These cases will be discussed in detail later. In the mean time it is well to remember that the key to an understanding of the whole matter is the careful drawing of figures.

Triangles must be solved in many fields such as astronomy, engineering, surveying, and architecture. A graphical construction is frequently all that is required. The triangle is carefully drawn to scale and the unknown parts measured. However this is not always sufficiently accurate. Particularly is this the case in astronomy. Yet, a drawing should always accompany every triangle solution. It guides us in Case IV and is a check on gross errors in all cases. It is also true that the problem will be better understood and its solution planned better if it is accompanied by a properly constructed figure.

The solution of a determined triangle by the use of the trigonometric functions is always possible. Usually this can be done in a variety of ways. A little ingenuity on the part of the student is all that is required. The solving of a problem involving the solution of triangles should be a challenge and not something to be done slavishly according to rules given in a book. However, the formulas which are given in the next section are very useful. They will be proved and should be memorized.

2. The Law of Sines and the Law of Cosines

(a) *The law of sines.*
Let us be given any triangle as in the figures.

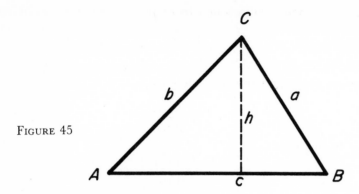

FIGURE 45

It is immediate that

$$b \sin A = h$$

and

$$a \sin B = h.$$

This is true in either figure since $\sin(180° - B) = \sin B$.

Hence

$$b \sin A = a \sin B. \tag{1}$$

Divide through by ab and we have

$$\frac{\sin A}{a} = \frac{\sin B}{b}. \tag{2}$$

Now a and b are any two sides of the triangle. Hence C and c can replace B and b in (2), or

$$\frac{\sin A}{a} = \frac{\sin C}{c}. \tag{3}$$

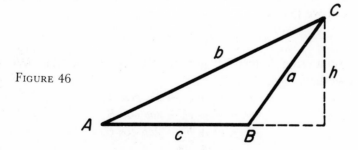

FIGURE 46

We combine these two formulas to write

$$\frac{\sin A}{a} = \frac{\sin B}{b} = \frac{\sin C}{c} \tag{4}$$

We can, of course, write (2) in the form

$$\frac{a}{b} = \frac{\sin A}{\sin B}$$

and (3) in the form

$$\frac{a}{c} = \frac{\sin A}{\sin B}.$$

These formulas are known as the **law of sines.**

It may be convenient to remember the law of sines in words as follows:

Two sides of a triangle have the same ratio as the sines of the opposite angles.

(b) *The Law of Cosines*

Again consider Figs. 45 and 46 and also remember that $\cos(180° - α) = -\cos α$. In either case

$$c = b \cos A + a \cos B.$$

We write this:

$$a \cos B = c - b \cos A. \tag{5}$$

But by the law of sines

$$a \sin B = b \sin A. \tag{6}$$

Square both sides of (5) and (6) and add

$$a^2(\sin^2 B + \cos^2 B) = c^2 - 2bc \cos A + b^2(\sin^2 A + \cos^2 A). \tag{7}$$

We know that for any $α$, $\sin^2 α + \cos^2 α = 1$. Make this substitution in (7) and we get

$$a^2 = b^2 + c^2 - 2bc \cos A.$$

By interchanging letters we get, in all, three formulas. We write them together:

$$\begin{aligned} a^2 &= b^2 + c^2 - 2bc \cos A; \\ b^2 &= a^2 + c^2 - 2ac \cos B; \\ c^2 &= a^2 + b^2 - 2ab \cos C. \end{aligned} \tag{8}$$

Formulas (8) are known as the **law of cosines.** This can be stated in words as follows:

The square of the length of any side of a triangle equals the sum of the squares of the lengths of the other two sides minus twice their product multiplied by the cosine of the angle included between them.

3. Solution of Triangles

Example 1: Given $a = 20.00$, $b = 25.00$, $C = 60°$. Solve the triangle.

We shall find c first. By the law of cosines

$$c^2 = a^2 + b^2 - 2ab \cos C;$$
$$c^2 = 400 + 625 - 2 \cdot 20 \cdot 25 \cdot \tfrac{1}{2} = 525;$$
$$c = 22.91.$$

We next find A. By the law of sines

$$\sin A = \frac{a}{c} \sin C = \frac{20}{22.91} \cdot (0.86603) = 0.7560;$$
$$A = 49° \; 7'.$$

Similarly,

$$\sin B = 25 \cdot \frac{\sin A}{a} = \frac{5}{4} \cdot (0.7560) = 0.9450;$$
$$B = 70° \; 53' \; 33''.$$

Check

$$180° = A + B + C = 180° \; 33''.$$

This is a very good check. However as a matter of fact the obtaining of seconds in an answer to this problem with c not calculated more accurately was a bit absurd. We consequently write

$$c = 22.91$$
$$A = 49° \; 7'$$
$$B = 70° \; 53'$$

Example 2: Given $b = 35.00$, $A = 98° \; 40'$, $C = 30° \; 55'$. Solve the triangle.

We find first.

$$B = 180° - (A + C) = 50° 25'.$$

We next find a. By the law of sines

$$a = b \frac{\sin A}{\sin B} = 35 \frac{0.98858}{0.77070};$$
$$a = 44.89.$$

We now find c.

$$c = b \frac{\sin C}{\sin B} = 35 \frac{0.51379}{0.77070};$$
$$c = 23.33.$$

We can feel fairly certain of the last digits in a and c, at least that the deviation from those given is not great.

Example 3: Given $a = 800.00$, $b = 1200.00$, $A = 34°$. Solve the triangle.

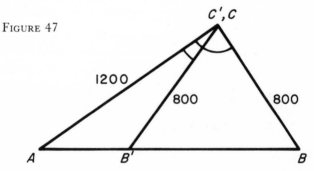

FIGURE 47

Figure 47 shows immediately that there are two triangles which contain the given parts, namely ABC and $AB'C$.

We use the law of sines to find

$$B = 57° 1'$$
$$B' = 180° - B = 122° 59'$$
$$C = 88° 59' \qquad C' = 23° 1'$$
$$c = 1430$$
$$c' = 559.4$$

4. *Solution of Oblique Triangles Without Remembering Formulas*

With the exercise of a little ingenuity it is possible to solve any triangle without the explicit use of any formula more complicated than those defining the trigonometric functions. A few examples illustrative of the kind of thing meant will be worked out.

Example 1:   Given $a = 20.00$, $b = 10.00$, $A = 75°$.   Solve   the triangle.

We first construct the triangle drawing in the altitude h.

FIGURE 48

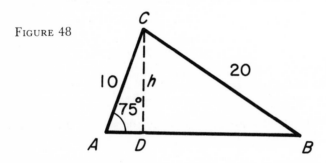

Even a hurried figure shows that there is one and but one triangle determined by the given data. Now $h = b \sin A = 10 \sin 75° = 9.659$. Then

$$\sin B = \frac{h}{a} = \frac{9.659}{20} = 0.4829$$
$$B = 28° \, 53'$$
$$180 - (A + B) = 76° \, 7'.$$

Next

$$c = AD + DB = 10 \cos 75° + 20 \cos (28° \, 53')$$
$$= 2.588 + 17.51 = 20.10$$

We write all our results together.

$$B = 28° \, 53'$$
$$C = 76° \, 7'$$
$$c = 20.10$$

Example 2:   Given $a = 5.00$, $b = 6.00$, $c = 9.00$. Solve the triangle.

Construct the triangle as indicated in the figure. Draw the altitude $CD = h$.

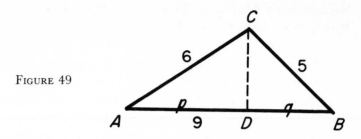

FIGURE 49

By the Pythagorean Theorem

$$h^2 = 36 - p^2, \text{ also } h^2 = 25 - q^2.$$

Hence

$$p^2 - q^2 = 11. \tag{1}$$

But

$$p + q = 9. \tag{2}$$

Divide the first of these equations by the second and we find

$$p - q = \tfrac{11}{9}. \tag{3}$$

Add this equation member by member to (2). We get

$$2p = 9 + \tfrac{11}{9} = \tfrac{92}{9}$$
$$p = \tfrac{46}{9}.$$

Substitute this in (2) and we get

$$q = \tfrac{35}{9}.$$

Now from the figure

$$\cos A = \frac{p}{6} = \frac{23}{27} = 0.8519.$$

From this

$$A = 31° \ 35'.$$

Also

$$\cos B = \frac{q}{a} = \frac{7}{9} = 0.7778$$
$$B = 38° \ 57'$$
$$C = 180° - (A + B) = 109° \ 28'.$$

The last problem, namely, given three sides of a triangle to solve for the angles, is the hardest type of triangle solution. If the student understands it, he should have no difficulty in understanding the solution of any triangle.

EXERCISES

Solve the triangles in Exercises 1 to 10 without the explicit use of either the law of sines or the law of cosines.

1. $A = 30°$, $B = 80°$, $a = 15$.
2. $A = 70°$, $a = 8$, $c = 5$.
3. $a = 2.3$, $b = 1.5$, $c = 1.6$.
4. $C = 100°$, $a = 82$, $c = 105$.
5. $b = 10$, $A = 85° \, 51'$, $B = 30°$.
6. $b = 97$, $B = 5° \, 33'$, $C = 153° \, 44'$.
7. $c = 90.52$, $C = 64° \, 51'$, $A = 71° \, 18'$.
8. $a = 3$, $b = 5$, $c = 7$.
9. $a = 5$, $b = 8$, $c = 9$.
10. $a = 10$, $b = 24$, $c = 6$.

Solve the following problems by any method.

11. From the top of a tower 30 feet high standing on level ground the angle of depression of a certain stone is 50° and of a second stone in line with the tower and first stone is 13°. How far apart are the stones?

12. Two points A and B are on opposite sides of an impassable swamp. At the point C, which is 456 feet from A and 580 feet from B, the angle subtended by the line AB is 44° 35'. What is the distance from A to B?

13. In the side of a hill which slopes upward at an angle of 14° a tunnel is bored downward at an angle of 12° with the horizontal. Find the vertical distance of a point 325 feet down the tunnel from the surface of the hill.

14. Two ships leave a wharf at the same time. One sails northeast at the rate of 8.5 miles an hour. The other sails north at the rate of 10 miles an hour. How far apart are they at the end of two hours?

15. A ladder 20 feet long is set with one end at a horizontal distance of 7 feet from a sloping wall. The other end of the ladder reaches 15 feet up the face of the wall. What angle does the wall make with the horizontal?

16. Three stations A, B, C are situated so that $AB = 300$ miles, $AC = 194$ miles, and $BC = 160$ miles, B being due north of C. Find the direction from B to A.

17. The diagonals of a parallelogram intersect at an angle of 52° 10.2'. One diagonal is 3325 feet and one side is 2995 feet. Find the other diagonal (two solutions).

18. Two points A and B are at opposite ends of a lake. To find the distance between them a point C is selected so that AC is 3472 feet and BC is 2956 feet. The angle ACB is found to be 46° 25'. What is the distance from A to B?

19. Along one bank of a straight river a surveyor lays off a base line 600 feet long with ends A and B. From each end of the line an object C on the opposite bank is sighted. The angles BAC and ABC are measured to be 62° 5.3′ and 81° 34.7′ respectively. Find the width of the river.

20. A chimney projects 6 feet above a roof. At a point 10 feet 8 inches down the roof from the base of the chimney, the chimney subtends an angle of 17° 40′. Find the angle at which the roof is inclined to the horizontal.

21. Two forces of 48 and 63 pounds respectively act on an object with an angle between them of 36° 55′. Find the magnitude of their resultant.

22. A plane is flying with a ground speed of 170 miles per hour and an air speed of 180 miles per hour. If the drift angle is 8°, what is the speed of the wind?

23. The observed time between the flash and the sound of a gun at post A is found to be 4.2 seconds, while at B which is 1500 feet from A it is 3.8 seconds. What is the angle from AB to the line of sight from A to the gun? The velocity of sound in air is 1100 feet per second approximately.

Chapter 17

Solutions of Triangles With the Aid of Logarithms

1. General

Solving triangles involves much multiplication and it may be that logarithms will aid in this work. However, the student should understand that logarithms are simply a tool to reduce the labor of computing. They do not really enter the problem. A computing machine may be far superior to a table of logarithms. At the same time formulas involving the sides and angles of a triangle have been developed which lend themselves readily to the use of logarithms. These are primarily to replace the law of cosines. The use of the law of cosines is very laborious if the numbers used involve many digits. The formulas in question will be derived in the next two sections.

2. Law of Tangents

The law of sines tells us that in any triangle

$$\frac{a}{c} = \frac{\sin A}{\sin C}, \quad \frac{b}{c} = \frac{\sin B}{\sin C}. \tag{1}$$

By subtracting the second of these from the first we get

$$\frac{a - b}{c} = \frac{\sin A - \sin B}{\sin C}. \tag{2}$$

Likewise by addition we get

$$\frac{a + b}{c} = \frac{\sin A + \sin B}{\sin C}. \tag{3}$$

Dividing each member of (2) by the corresponding member of (3) we have

$$\frac{a - b}{a + b} = \frac{\sin A - \sin B}{\sin A + \sin B}. \tag{4}$$

If now we apply formulas (29) and (28) of Chapter 7 respectively to the numerator and denominator of the right hand member of (4) we get

$$\frac{a - b}{a + b} = \frac{2 \cos \frac{1}{2} (A + B) \sin \frac{1}{2} (A - B)}{2 \sin \frac{1}{2} (A + B) \cos \frac{1}{2} (A - B)}$$
$$= \tan \tfrac{1}{2} (A - B) \cot \tfrac{1}{2} (A + B).$$

Hence

$$\frac{a - b}{a + b} = \frac{\tan \frac{1}{2} (A - B)}{\tan \frac{1}{2} (A + B)}. \tag{5}$$

Interchanging letters:

$$\frac{a - c}{a + c} = \frac{\tan \frac{1}{2} (A - C)}{\tan \frac{1}{2} (A + C)}, \tag{5'}$$

$$\frac{b - c}{b + c} = \frac{\tan \frac{1}{2} (B - C)}{\tan \frac{1}{2} (B + C)}. \tag{5''}$$

Formulas (5), (5′), (5″) are known as the **"law of tangents."**

3. *Half-Angle Formulas*

From the law of cosines

$$\cos A = \frac{b^2 + c^2 - a^2}{2bc}.$$

But, by formulas (25) and (26) of Chapter 7, if A is any angle

$$2 \sin^2\tfrac{1}{2}A = 1 - \cos A \text{ and } 2 \cos^2\tfrac{1}{2} A = 1 + \cos A.$$

Hence for the A of our triangle

$$2 \sin^2\tfrac{1}{2}A = 1 - \frac{b^2 + c^2 - a^2}{2bc}$$

$$= \frac{2bc - b^2 - c^2 + a^2}{2bc}$$

$$= \frac{a^2 - (b^2 - 2bc + c^2)}{2bc}$$

$$= \frac{a^2 - (b - c)^2}{2bc}$$

$$= \frac{[a + (b - c)][a - (b - c)]}{2bc}$$

$$= \frac{[a + b - c][a - b + c]}{2bc}$$

Hence

$$\sin \tfrac{1}{2}A = \sqrt{\frac{(a + b - c)(a - b + c)}{4bc}} \tag{6}$$

$$2 \cos^2\tfrac{1}{2}A = 1 + \frac{b^2 + c^2 - a^2}{2bc}$$

$$= \frac{2bc + b^2 + c^2 - a^2}{2bc}$$

$$= \frac{(b + c)^2 - a^2}{2bc}$$

$$= \frac{(b + c + a)(b + c - a)}{2bc}$$

Hence

$$\cos \tfrac{1}{2}A = \sqrt{\frac{(b + c + a)(b + c - a)}{4bc}} \tag{7}$$

In both cases the sign before the radical is plus since half the angle of a triangle is always less than a right angle.

These formulas give the sine and cosine of one-half the angle of a triangle in terms of the lengths of its sides.

If we let

$$2s = a + b + c,$$

then

$$a + b - c = 2(s - c)$$
$$a - b + c = 2(s - b).$$

This permits us to write formulas (6) and (7) in more compact form.

$$\sin \tfrac{1}{2}A = \sqrt{\frac{(s - b)(s - c)}{bc}}. \tag{8}$$

$$\cos \tfrac{1}{2}A = \sqrt{\frac{s(s - a)}{bc}}. \tag{9}$$

Interchanging letters we get

$$\sin \tfrac{1}{2}B = \sqrt{\frac{(s - c)(s - a)}{ca}}, \tag{8'}$$

$$\cos \tfrac{1}{2}B = \sqrt{\frac{s(s - b)}{ca}}, \tag{9'}$$

$$\sin \tfrac{1}{2}C = \sqrt{\frac{(s - a)(s - b)}{ab}}, \tag{8''}$$

$$\cos \tfrac{1}{2}C = \sqrt{\frac{s(s - c)}{ab}}, \tag{9''}$$

If we let $r = \sqrt{\dfrac{(s - a)(s - b)(s - c)}{s}}$,

we readily prove that

$$\tan \tfrac{1}{2}A = \frac{r}{s - a}, \tag{10}$$

$$\tan \tfrac{1}{2}B = \frac{r}{s - b}. \tag{10'}$$

$$\tan \tfrac{1}{2}C = \frac{r}{s - c}. \tag{10''}$$

4. *The Four Cases*

Case I: *Given two angles and the included side.*

No new methods are introduced. Solution is by means of the law of sines. The computation can be carried out by means of logarithms.

Case II: *Given two sides and the angle opposite one of them.*

This is the so called **ambiguous case.** We shall see that there may be no triangle with the given parts, that there may be one and only one triangle with the given parts or there may be exactly two different triangles with the given parts. This is illustrated in the figures below.

Let us be given A, b and a. Suppose $a < b \sin A$. Here there is no solution to the problem, because $b \sin A = h$ and a is not long enough to reach C.

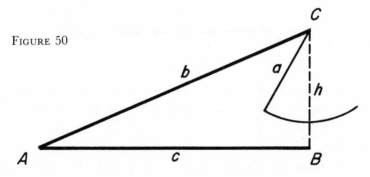

FIGURE 50

Suppose $a = b \sin A$. Here there is one and only one solution, namely the right triangle.

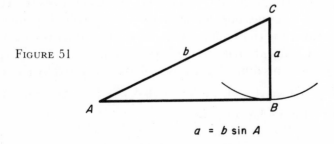

FIGURE 51

$$a = b \sin A$$

Suppose $a \geq b$. Here there is just one solution as indicated in the figure.

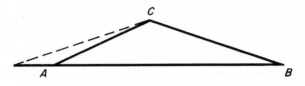

FIGURE 52

Suppose $b > a > b \sin A$. Here there are two solutions as indicated in the figure namely the triangle ABC and the triangle $AB'C$: Note that $B' = 180° - B$.

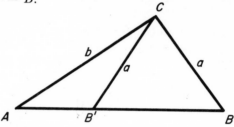

FIGURE 53

The solution of triangles that fall under Case II is best carried out by means of the law of sines. Logarithms can be used in the computation.

Case III: *Given two sides and the included angle.*

The most natural formula to employ is the law of cosines which gives us the third side. A second angle is then found by the law of sines. The third angle can also be found by means of the law of sines or more simply by utilization of the fact that the sum of the three angles of a triangle is 180°. However, we have already remarked that the law of cosines does not lend itself to logarithmic computation. This is because the right hand member is a sum rather than a product. The law of tangents has been introduced for the very purpose of getting around this difficulty. Its use will be illustrated by an example.

Example: Given $A = 83° \, 44'$, $b = 78.4$, $c = 61.3$. Solve the triangle.

Solution: By the law of tangents

$$\frac{b - c}{b + c} = \frac{\tan \frac{1}{2}(B - C)}{\tan \frac{1}{2}(B + C)}.$$

Substitute and we get

$$\frac{78.4 - 61.3}{78.4 + 61.3} = \frac{\tan \frac{1}{2}(B - C)}{\tan \frac{1}{2}(180° - 83° 44')}.$$

From this

$$\tan \tfrac{1}{2}(B - C) = \frac{(17.1)(\tan 48° 8')}{139.7},$$

$$\log 17.1 = 1.23300,$$
$$\log \tan 48° 8' = 0.04760$$
$$0.04760 + 1.23300 = 11.28060 - 10$$
$$\log 139.7 = 2.14520,$$
$$\log \tan \tfrac{1}{2}(B - C) = 9.13540 - 10,$$
$$\tfrac{1}{2}(B - C) = 7° 46' 26'',$$
$$\tfrac{1}{2}(B + C) = 48° 8' = \tfrac{1}{2}(180° - A).$$

Add and we have

$$B = 55° 54' 26''.$$

Subtract and we get

$$C = 40° 21' 24''.$$

To find a we use the law of sines.

$$a = \frac{b \sin A}{\sin B}$$
$$a = 94.10.$$

Case IV: *Given the three sides.*

We shall illustrate the solution of such triangles with the aid of logarithms by means of an example.

Example: $a = 32.452$, $b = 41.728$, $c = 53.981$. Find A, B, C.

$$2s = 32.452 + 41.728 + 53.981$$
$$s = 64.080$$
$$s - a = 31.628$$
$$s - b = 22.352$$
$$s - c = 10.099$$
$$r = \sqrt{\frac{(31.628)(22.352)(10.099)}{64.080}}$$

$$\log 31.628 = 1.50007$$
$$\log 22.352 = 1.34932$$
$$\log 10.099 = 1.00428$$
$$\overline{\phantom{\log 10.099 = {}} 3.85367}$$

$$\log 64.080 \ = 1.80672$$
$$\log r^2 \qquad = 2.04695$$
$$\log r \qquad = 11.02348 - 10$$
$$\log (s - a) \ = 1.50007$$

$$\tan \frac{A}{2} = \frac{x}{s-a}$$

$$\log \tan \frac{A}{2} = 9.52341 - 10$$

$$\frac{A}{2} = 18° \ 27' \ 21''$$

$$A = 36° \ 54' \ 42''$$

$$\tan \tfrac{1}{2} B = \frac{r}{s-b}$$

$$\log r \qquad = 11.02348 - 10$$
$$\log (s - b) \ = 1.34932$$
$$\log \tan \tfrac{1}{2} B = 9.67416 - 10$$

$$\frac{B}{2} = 25° \ 16' \ 42''$$

$$B = 50° \ 33' \ 24''$$

Similarly,

$$\tan \frac{C}{2} = \frac{r}{s-c},$$

$$\log \tan \frac{C}{2} = 0.01920,$$

$$\frac{C}{2} = 46° \ 15' \ 58'',$$

$$C = 92° \ 31' \ 56''.$$

Check $A + B + C = 36° \ 54' \ 42'' + 50° \ 33' \ 24'' + 92° \ 31' \ 56'' = 180° \ 0' \ 2''$.

EXERCISES

1. $a = 33.46$, $b = 62.24$, $c = 53.88$. Find B.

2. $a = 29.31$, $b = 18.92$, $C = 50° \ 7' \ 10''$. Find A, B, c.

3. Is it possible for a triangular building lot at the intersection of two streets to have a frontage on one street of 264 feet, a frontage on the other of 135 feet and a third side of 400 feet?

Solve the triangles given in exercises 4 to 12.

4.	$a = 0.2960$,	$b = 0.1008$,	$C = 64° 48'$.
5.	$b = 56.68$,	$c = 64.40$,	$A = 98° 10'$.
6.	$a = 3820$,	$b = 1901$,	$c = 2985$.
7.	$a = 0.01462$,	$b = 0.01939$,	$c = 0.02465$.
8.	$a = 13.29$,	$b = 22.754$,	$c = 25.005$.
9.	$a = 276.3$,	$b = 199.9$,	$C = 57° 35'$.
10.	$a = 124.23$,	$b = 101.77$,	$C = 69°$.
11.	$a = 0.06139$,	$A = 35° 9'$,	$C = 26° 53'$.
12.	$b = 23.30$,	$A = 50° 42.9'$,	$B = 68° 9.4'$.

13. From two successive milestones in a straight horizontal road the angles of elevation of a balloon are 48° 18.7′ and 37° 49.6′. Find the height of the balloon if it is directly above the road at a point between the milestones.

14. A building, 75.2 feet high, stands at the end of a street which slopes down at an angle of 6° 52′ with the horizontal. What is the angle of elevation of the top of the building at a point on the street 100 feet from the foot of the building?

15. Two streets meet at an angle of 57° 30′. A triangular lot has frontage of 110.9 and 120.2 feet respectively on the two streets. Find the angles which the rear side of the lot makes with the two streets.

16. Two forces of 76.4 and 88.6 pounds respectively act on an object and in directions that make an angle of 62° 10′ the one with the other. Find the magnitude of their resultant and the angle that it makes with each of the given forces.

17. A tunnel is to be bored under a hill and the distance from one end P to the other end Q is desired. A third point R is chosen and measurements are taken as follows: $RP = 684.6$ feet. $RQ = 911.8$ feet. Angle $PRQ = 58° 28'$. Find the distance PQ.

18. Two forces of 812.6 and 900.0 pounds respectively are applied at a point and have a resultant of 1257 pounds. What angle do the two forces make with each other?

19. An aviator's ground speed is due east 185 miles per hour. The wind is blowing from the southeast at a speed of 15 miles per hour. In what direction and with what speed would he be going if the wind stopped blowing?

20. A triangle is inscribed in a circle. The lengths of its sides are 14, 21 and 28 inches. What percentage of the circumference is the arc subtended by the largest side of the triangle?

Chapter 18

Complex Numbers

1. Definition

Consider the ordinary numbers with which we have been dealing in this book. They are called *real numbers*. This is a very unfortunate term because it implies that there are other numbers which have an unreal or ghostly nature. Now all numbers are alike in the sense that they are tools made by man for carrying on his mathematics. The student probably will recall when fractions were added to the numbers of his childhood and then when the negative numbers were added to the numbers that he already used. The set of numbers composed of the positive and negative integers and zero and the fractions, both proper and improper, are called the *rational* numbers. Each one of them is called a rational number. Thus, 0, 1, 4/5, 17/11, 0.15, 3.14 are rational numbers.

The student may recollect that he has worked with certain other numbers that are not rational (Chapter 1, Section 1). A number that is not rational is of course termed *irrational*.

The rational and irrational numbers together constitute the real numbers. Out of the real numbers we may make new numbers which we call complex numbers. Each ordered pair of real numbers in fact defines a complex number, much as the way in which fractions are defined in terms of the integers. Before the complex numbers can be useful, however, we must define operations of arithmetic with them so that we can use them in our mathematics.

DEFINITION: *The ordered pairs of real numbers* (a, b) *subject to the rules of arithmetic which follow are called* **complex numbers.**

DEFINITIONS: $(a, b) = (c, d)$ if and only if $a = c$, $b = d$.

$(a, b) + (c, d) = (a + c, b + d)$.
$(a, b) - (c, d) = (a - c, b - d)$.
$(a, b) \times (c, d) = (ac - bd, ad + bc)$.
$(a, b) \div (c, d) = \left(\dfrac{ac + bd}{c^2 + d^2}, \dfrac{bc - ad}{c^2 + d^2} \right)$, $c^2 + d^2 \neq 0$

Of course the rules for subtraction and division are not independent of those for addition and multiplication.

To subtract a complex number (c, d) from a complex number (a, b) means to find all numbers which when added to (c, d) give (a, b). We readily prove that there is only one such number and that it is given by the above formula.

Similarly, the rule for division is a consequence of the rule for multiplication. To divide one complex number by a second means to find that complex number which when multiplied by the second yields the first.

We shall work out the rule for division. Suppose,

$$(a, b) = (c, d)(A, B).$$

Then

$$(a, b) = cA - dB, cB + dA)$$

Hence

$$a = cA - dB$$
$$b = cB + dA.$$

We solve these equations for A and B and find the given forms. These forms are both necessary and sufficient. This means that A and B must have the given form and that if they do then $(c, d) \times (A, B) = (a, b)$. The student should verify this. He will also observe that c, d) $\times$ $(A,\ B)$ = $(A,\ B)$ $\times$ $(c,\ d)$. He will observe that if c = d = 0 the denominators vanish and A and B are not defined, since we cannot divide by zero.

The definitions that we have given cause the complex number system to obey the following laws of arithmetic that we have been using in all our work. Let A, B, C be any complex numbers.

   I. *Commutative law of addition* $A+B=B+A.$
  II. *Commutative law of multiplication* $A\times B=B\times A.$
 III. *Associative law of addition* $A+(B+C)=(A+B)+C.$
 IV. *Associative law of multiplication* $(A\times B)\times C=A\times(B\times C).$
  V. *Distributive law of multiplication* $A\times(B+C)=A\times B+A\times C.$
           with reference to addition

We shall prove I. Let A = $(a,\ b)$ and B = $(c,\ d)$. Then

$$A + B = (a + c,\ b + d),$$
$$B + A = (c + a,\ d + b).$$

But these are equal since $a + c = c + a$ and $b + d = d + b$. Remember that a, b, c, d are real.

DEFINITION: *The complex number* $(a,\ b)$ *is called zero, if and only if* $a = 0$ *and* $b = 0$.

EXERCISE

Prove laws II, III, IV, and V.

2. The Imaginary Unit

Consider those complex numbers where the second number is 0, that is all complex numbers of the form $(x,\ 0)$. We immediately verify that

$$(a,\ 0) + (c,\ 0) = (a + c,\ 0)$$
$$(a,\ 0) \times (c,\ 0) = (ac,\ 0)$$
$$(a,\ 0) - (c,\ 0) = (a - c,\ 0)$$
$$(a,\ 0)/(c,\ 0) = (a/c.\ 0),\ c \neq 0.$$

We note from these relations that, so far as arithmetic among themselves is concerned, the complex numbers $(x, 0)$ behave exactly as do the real numbers. Consequently for purposes of arithmetic we shall write $(x, 0)$ simply as x,

$$(x, 0) = x.$$

We shall call these numbers the real complex numbers or just real numbers.

Next consider the complex numbers with the first number 0, namely the complex numbers of the form $(0, y)$. We verify that

$$(0, b) + (0, d) = (0, b + d).$$
$$(0, b) \times (0, d) = (-bd, 0).$$
$$(0, b) - (0, d) = (0, b - d).$$
$$(0, b) \div (0, d) = (b/d, 0), d \neq 0.$$

We note in particular that

$$(0, 1) \times (0, 1) = (-1, 0).$$

Now let us denote $(0, 1)$ by i

$$i = (0, 1).$$

Then

$$i^2 = (-1, 0).$$

But we have agreed to write this as -1. Consequently,

$$i^2 = -1.$$

The numbers $(0, y)$ can now be written yi. This, so to speak, conforms to all our rules of arithmetic and makes these rules easy to remember. The numbers yi are called the **pure imaginary numbers** or simply the **imaginary numbers.** The name is usually very misleading to the beginner. We repeat that they are no more or less "imaginary" than other numbers. If regarded simply as a technical term, the word *imaginary* is as good as any other.

The number $i = (0, 1)$ is called the **imaginary unit.**

We next note that

$$(x, 0) + (0, y) = (x, y).$$

Hence we write (x, y) simply as $x + yi$:

$$(x + yi = (x, y).$$

We find all our rules for arithmetic of complex numbers follow from the rules for working with binomials, *and indeed this was their historical origin.*

The student will find it convenient in most of his work to replace (x, y) by $x + yi$. The advantage is that the rules of arithmetic are more easily remembered. There are disadvantages. For example there is no distinction in notation between the binomial $(x, 0) + (0, y)$ and the single number (x, y). This, however, is a frequent situation. Thus $\frac{1}{2}$ may denote $1 \div 2$ or the number one-half. Also the complex numbers do not appear as a new set but rather as an addition to the real numbers of new numbers, $a + bi$, $b \neq 0$. This point of view, although the less desirable in a systematic development of the number system, represents what actually took place historically.

EXERCISES

Perform the indicated operations:

1. $(1, 3) + (4, 5)$
2. $(6, 7) - (3, 2)$
3. $(-8, 4) - (-10, 11)$
4. $(2, 3) \times (7, 8)$
5. $(-2, 3) \times (-4, 7)$
6. $(\sqrt{2}, \sqrt{3}) \times (\sqrt{3}, \sqrt{2})$
7. $(-1/2, 4) \times (7, 6)$
8. $(a + b, c - d) \times (1/a, 1/b)$
9. $(2, 4) \div (6, 3)$
10. $(6, 3) \div (2, 4)$
11. $(4, 2) \div (\frac{1}{2}, \frac{1}{2})$
12. $(a - b, c - d) \div (a^2 - b^2, c^2 - d^2)$
13. $(2 + 3i) + (6 - 4i)$
14. $(6 - 2i) - (3 - 4i)$
15. $(7 + 6i) \times (8 - 4i)$
16. $(7 + 6i) \div (1 + i)$
17. $(3 + 2i) \div (7 + 6i)$
18. $(a - bi) \div (c - di)$
19. i^2
20. i^3
21. i^4
22. i^5
23. i^{17}
24. i^{101}
25. $(2 + i)^6$
26. $(\frac{1}{2} + i)^{10}$
27. $(a + bi)^8$
28. $(a + bi)^{12}$
29. $(1 + i)^{10} \div (1 - i)^{15}$
30. $(2 + i)^4 \div (6 - i)^8$

In Exercises 31 to 34 assume x and y to be real:

31. If $3x + 4y - i(x - y) = 2 - 3i$, find x and y.
32. If $x + yi = 4 - 3i$, find x and y.
33. If $(7x - 8y) + i(2x - y) = 1 + yi$, find x and y.
34. If $7x + 8y - i(2x - y) = 1 - yi$, find x and y.

3. Polar Form of Complex Numbers

Consider the complex number, $a + bi$. Let us multiply and divide it by $\sqrt{a^2 + b^2}$; we get

$$a + bi = \sqrt{a^2 + b^2}\left[\frac{a}{\sqrt{a^2 + b^2}} + \frac{bi}{\sqrt{a^2 + b^2}}\right],$$

a and b not both zero.

Since $\left(\dfrac{a}{\sqrt{a^2 + b^2}}\right)^2 + \left(\dfrac{b}{\sqrt{a^2 + b^2}}\right)^2 = 1$, we can let

$$\frac{a}{\sqrt{a^2 + b^2}} = \cos\,\theta.$$

$$\frac{b}{\sqrt{a^2 + b^2}} = \sin\,\theta.$$

and can always determine θ. If in addition we let

$$\sqrt{a^2 + b^2} = r,$$

we can write

$$a + bi = r(\cos\,\theta + i \sin\,\theta). \tag{1}$$

This is called the polar form of the complex number. We give the name **modulus** or **absolute value** to r. The term *absolute value* is to be preferred, although both terms represent good usage. Similarly θ is called the **amplitude** or **angle** of the complex number. The word *angle* is probably to be preferred.

Example 1

$$1 + i = \sqrt{2}\left(\frac{1}{\sqrt{2}} + \frac{1}{\sqrt{2}}i\right) = 2\left(\cos\frac{\pi}{4} + i \sin\frac{\pi}{4}\right).$$

In place of $\pi/4$ we can write $\pi/4 + 2n\pi$ and we have the more general result.

$$1 + i = \sqrt{2}\left[\cos\left(\frac{\pi}{4} + 2n\pi\right) + i \sin\left(\frac{\pi}{4} + 2n\pi\right)\right].$$

Example 2

$$\left(\frac{1}{2} + \frac{\sqrt{3}}{2}i\right) = 1\left[\cos\left(\frac{\pi}{3} + 2n\pi\right) + i \sin\left(\frac{\pi}{3} + 2n\pi\right)\right].$$

EXERCISES

Write the following complex numbers in polar form. Use tables if necessary.

1. $-\frac{1}{2} - \frac{3}{2}i$ 2. $(1 - i)$
3. $(-1 + i)$ 4. $\sqrt{\frac{3}{2}} + \frac{1}{2}i$
5. $1 + 0i$ 6. 1
7. i 8. $-i$
9. $3 + 4i$ 10. $(-1 + 2i)$
11. $(6 - 8i)$ 12. $\frac{1}{2} + \frac{1}{3}i$

4. *Graphical Representation of Complex Numbers*

A complex number, $a + bi$, consists of two parts, a and b. Here a is called the **real part** and b the **imaginary part.** This pair of numbers can be pictorially represented by the point having abscissa a and ordinate b. Thus every complex number is pictured by a point, and every point in the plane has a corresponding complex number.

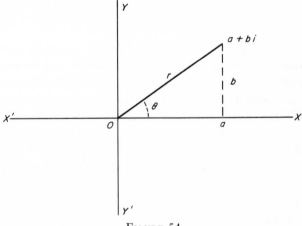

FIGURE 54

Just as the complex numbers can be represented by points in the plane, so they can be represented by vectors. These vectors are usually drawn with tails at the origin, although this is not necessary. The complex number $(a, b) = a + bi$ is represented by the radius-vector with component a along the *axis of reals* (x-axis) and a component b along the *axis of imaginaries* (y-axis). The r and θ of the polar form show up well in this representation. We see that

r = length of radius vector of (a, b)

θ = angle made by the radius vector with the x-axis.

Thus r is the length of the hypotenuse of the right triangle of which a and b are the length of the legs.

EXERCISES

Represent graphically the following complex numbers.

1. $(2 + 3i)$ 2. $(1 - 4i)$
3. $(0 + 2i)$ 4. $(2 + 0i)$
5. 2 6. $3i$

7. $10\left[\cos \dfrac{\pi}{4} + i \sin \dfrac{\pi}{4}\right]$ 8. $15\left(\cos \dfrac{\pi}{6} + i \sin \dfrac{\pi}{6}\right)$

9. $12(\cos 0.2 + i \sin 0.2)$ 10. $4(\cos 5.76 + i \sin 5.76)$

5. *Graphical Addition and Subtraction of Complex Numbers*

The radius-vector representation of complex numbers lends itself readily to geometrical addition and subtraction, which in turn has certain applications in the general theory of vectors.

Construction: To add $a + bi$ and $c + di$, construct the corresponding radius-vectors with common origin at the origin of coordinates. The sum radius-vector $(a + bi) + (c + di)$ is $(a + c) + i(b + d)$, which in turn is the diagonal of the parallelogram with the radius-vectors $(a + bi)$ and $(c + di)$ as sides. Proof follows very easily from Figure 55.

$OM = RT$ since RP is equal in length and parallel to OJ. Consequently,

$$OD = ON + ND = ON + RT = ON + OM = a + c.$$

Similarly

$$DP = b + d.$$

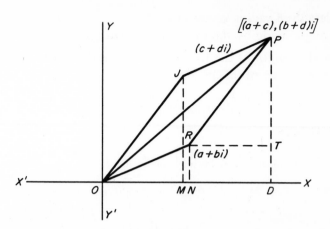

FIGURE 55

The construction of the diagonal (sum) radius-vector is simple with proper instruments. It is easily done by putting the tail of one vector on the head of the other. This is the so called triangular method. If a number of vectors are to be added, we just construct them in order, with tail on head (Fig. 56). Here $OP_4 = OP_1 + P_1P_2 + P_2P_3 + P_3P_4$.

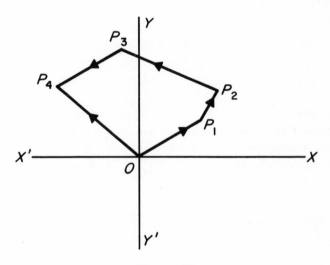

FIGURE 56

Subtraction is best performed by reversing the sense of the vector to be subtracted, and adding.

EXERCISES

1. $(2 + i) + (4 + 3i)$ 2. $(3 - i) + (6 - 2i)$

3. $(2 + i) + (4 + 3i) + (6 + 2i) + (7 + 8i)$

4. $(2 + 3i) - (4 + 3i)$ 5. $(2 + 3i) + (5 - i) - (7 + i) + (2 + 4i)$

6. $7\left[\cos\dfrac{\pi}{4} + i \sin\dfrac{\pi}{4}\right] + 6\left[\cos\dfrac{\pi}{3} + i \sin\dfrac{\pi}{3}\right]$

7. $2\left[\cos\dfrac{\pi}{3} + i \sin\dfrac{\pi}{3}\right] - 4\left[\cos\dfrac{\pi}{2} + i \sin\dfrac{\pi}{2}\right]$

8. $10(\cos 30° + i \sin 30°) + 8(\cos 45° + i \sin 45°)$

9. $3(\cos 725° + i \sin 725°) - 5(\cos 1000° + i \sin 1000°)$

10. $3(\cos(-240°) + i \sin(-240°)) - 5(\cos(-700°) + i \sin(-700°))$

6. *Arithmetic with Complex Numbers in Polar Form*

Writing complex numbers in polar form simplifies greatly some of the operations of arithmetic with them. This is notably true of raising to powers and extracting roots. Sometimes multiplication and division are also abbreviated.

Let us multiply $r_1(\cos \theta_1 + i \sin \theta_1)$ by $r_2(\cos \theta_2 + i \sin \theta_2)$. We carry out the multiplication and find

$$r_1(\cos \theta_1 + i \sin \theta_1) \times r_2(\cos \theta_2 + i \sin \theta_2) =$$
$$r_1 r_2[(\cos \theta_1 \cos \theta_2 - \sin \theta_1 \sin \theta_2) + i(\sin \theta_1 \cos \theta_2 + \cos \theta_1 \sin \theta_2)]$$

We refer now to formulas (1) and (3) of Chapter 7, and see that we can write this as

$$r_1(\cos \theta_1 + i \sin \theta_1) \times r_2(\cos \theta_2 + i \sin \theta_2) =$$
$$r_1 r_2[\cos(\theta_1 + \theta_2) + i \sin(\theta_1 + \theta_2)]$$

The product of two complex numbers is a new complex number whose absolute value is the product of the absolute values of the two given complex numbers and whose amplitude is the sum of their amplitudes.

To divide A by B means to find the number which when multiplied by B yields A. This immediately gives us the following formula and rule.

$$r_1(\cos \theta_1 + i \sin \theta_1) \div r_2(\cos \theta_2 + i \sin \theta_2)$$

$$\frac{r_1}{r_2}[\cos(\theta_1 - \theta_2) + i \sin(\theta_1 - \theta_2)], \ r_2 \neq 0$$

In words, we have the following:

The quotient obtained by dividing one complex number by a second, different from zero, is a complex number whose absolute value is obtained by dividing the absolute value of the first by the absolute value of the second and whose amplitude is obtained by subtracting the amplitude of the second from the amplitude of the first.

We also have the following formula for raising to an integral power

$$[r(\cos \theta + i \sin \theta)]^n = r^n(\cos n\theta + i \sin n\theta).$$

The problem of taking roots is important and it is also a bit complicated so it is treated under a separate heading.

7. *Roots of Complex Numbers*

Given

$$z^n = A \tag{2}$$

to find z.

The following are some simple special cases.

(a) $z^2 = 4$
   $z = \pm 2$
(b) $z^2 = -1$
   $z = \pm i$
(c) $z^4 = 1$
   $z = 1, \ -1, \ i, \ -i.$

These special cases lead us to suspect that if $n > 1$ there is more than one answer to the problem. Those of us who remember our work in algebra headed "Theory of Equations" will recognize equation (2) as an equation of the nth degree and will know that it will have n roots. We suspect that they are all distinct, since this is the case in the examples that we have seen. Our problem is to find these roots. The problem is solved by means of the following theorem:

Theorem I: *If $A = r(\cos A + i \sin \theta) \neq 0$ then there are n distinct numbers which satisfy (2). These are given by the following formulas. There are no other numbers which satisfy (2). Let θ by a particular determination of the angle.*

$$z_1 = \sqrt[n]{r}\left[\cos\frac{\theta}{n} + i\sin\frac{\theta}{n}\right]$$

$$z_2 = \sqrt[n]{r}\left[\cos\frac{\theta + 2\pi}{n} + i\sin\frac{\theta + 2\pi}{n}\right]$$

$$z_3 = \sqrt[n]{r}\left[\cos\frac{\theta + 2(2\pi)}{n} + i\sin\frac{\theta + 2(2\pi)}{n}\right]$$

. . . .

$$z_n = \sqrt[n]{r}\left[\cos\frac{\theta + (n-1)2\pi}{n} + i\sin\frac{\theta + (n-1)2\pi}{n}\right]$$

We prove that the numbers $z_1, z_2, z_3, \ldots, z_n$ satisfy (2) simply by applying the rule for raising a complex number to an integral power. They are all different because no one of them is zero and their angles are not congruent. Moreover, we learned in our algebra course that a polynomial equation of nth degree cannot have more than n roots. This completes the proof of the theorem.

If we plot the points $z_1, z_2, z_3, \ldots, z_n$ in the complex plane, the points which we obtain are the vertices of a regular polygon of n sides with center at the origin. This follows from the fact that each of them has the same absolute value and that the amplitude of each differs from that of the next by $\frac{2\pi}{n}$, plotted as radians. We note particularly that $\sqrt[n]{r}$ denotes the positive real nth root of r.

Example 1

$$z^3 = 1$$

$$z_1 = 1\left[\cos\frac{0}{3} + i\sin\frac{0}{3}\right] = 1$$

$$z_2 = 1\left[\cos\frac{2\pi}{3} + i\sin\frac{2\pi}{3}\right] = -\frac{1}{2} + \sqrt{\frac{3}{2}}i$$

$$z_3 = 1\left[\cos\frac{4\pi}{3} + i\sin\frac{4\pi}{3}\right] = -\frac{1}{2} - \sqrt{\frac{3}{2}}i$$

The numbers which we have denoted here by z_2 and z_3 are frequently called ω and ω^2. They have the interesting property that either one of them squared yields the other.

Example 2

$$z^5 = 32$$
$$z_1 = 2(\cos 0 + i \sin 0) = 2.$$

$$z_2 = 2\left(\cos \frac{2\pi}{5} + i \sin \frac{2\pi}{5}\right) = 2(0.30902 + i0.95106)$$

$$z_3 = 2\left(\cos \frac{4\pi}{5} + i \sin \frac{4\pi}{5}\right) = 2(-0.80902 + i0.58779)$$

$$z_4 = 2\left(\cos \frac{6\pi}{5} + i \sin \frac{6\pi}{5}\right) = 2(-0.80902 - i0.58770)$$

$$z_5 = 2\left(\cos \frac{8\pi}{5} + i \sin \frac{8\pi}{5}\right) = 2(0.30902 - i0.95106)$$

The values in the right-hand column are taken from tables. We notice that $z_2^2 = 2z_3$, $z_2^3 = 4z_4$, $z_2^4 = 8z_5$, $z_2^5 = 16z_1 = 32$. Similar relationships hold for each of the other z's.

Example 3

$$z^3 = 1 + i = \sqrt{2}\left[\cos \frac{\pi}{4} + i \sin \frac{\pi}{4}\right]$$

$$z_1 = \sqrt[6]{2}\left[\cos \frac{\pi}{12} + i \sin \frac{\pi}{12}\right]$$

$$z_2 = \sqrt[6]{2}\left[\cos \frac{9\pi}{12} + i \sin \frac{9\pi}{12}\right]$$

$$z_3 = \sqrt[6]{2}\left[\cos \frac{17\pi}{12} + i \sin \frac{17\pi}{12}\right]$$

Tables can be used to write these in decimals if desired. Looking up the trigonometric functions in a table written in degrees we interpret $\frac{\pi}{12}$, $\frac{9\pi}{12}$, $\frac{17\pi}{12}$ as angles in radian measure. This radian measure must be reduced to degrees. Thus,

$$\frac{\pi}{12} = 15°, \quad \frac{9\pi}{12} = 135°, \quad \frac{17\pi}{12} = 255°.$$

EXERCISES

Solve completely the equations in Exercises 1 to 12.

1. $z^6 = 64$ 2. $z^7 = 128$ 3. $z^8 = 256$

4. $z^3 = 2 + 3i$ 5. $z^4 = -1$ 6. $z^7 = 1$

7. $z^7 = -1$ 8. $z^7 = i$ 9. $z^8 = 256i$

10. $z^{10} = 1 + i$ 11. $z^5 = -2 + 3i$ 12. $z^5 = -1$

13. If $z^6 = 64$, plot all possible values for z as points in the complex plane. Plot these values as vectors.

14. If $z^3 = 1$ has roots 1, z_1 and z_2, prove that $z_1^2 = z_2$ and $z_2^2 = z_1$.

15. The equation $z^9 = 1$ has roots 1, z_1, ... , z_8. What are they? Plot them as points in the complex plane. Find z_2^2, z_2^3, ... , z_2^8, z_3^2, z_3^3, ... , z_3^8. Comment on your result.

16. Generalize Exercise 15 by changing z^9 to z^n.

8. *Applications of Vector Representation of Complex Numbers*

The vector representation of complex numbers leads to many applications. A few examples and exercises illustrative of the kind of thing involved are given.

Example 1: Forces of six pounds, eight pounds, and ten pounds in the same plane act on a particle at angles of 30°, 45° and 60° with the x-axis. What is their resultant?

$$F_1 = 6(\cos 30° + i \sin 30°) = 3\sqrt{3} + i3$$
$$F_2 = 8(\cos 45° + i \sin 45°) = 4\sqrt{2} + i4\sqrt{2}$$
$$F_3 = 10(\cos 60° + i \sin 60°) = 5 + i5\sqrt{3}$$

$$F = \text{resultant force} = (3\sqrt{3} + 4\sqrt{2} + 5) + i(3 + 4\sqrt{2} + 5\sqrt{3})$$
$$= 15.853 + i17.317$$
$$F = \sqrt{(15.853)^2 + (17.317)^2}\left[\cos \tan^{-1} \frac{17.317}{15.853} + \sin \tan^{-1} \frac{17.317}{15.853}\right]$$
$$= 23.5[\cos (47° \ 30') + i \sin (47° \ 30')]$$

Example 2: An airplane has an air speed of 400 miles per hour in a northwest direction. There is a steady wind of ten miles per hour in a direction 10° north of west. What is the ground speed of the plane?

$$\text{Air speed} = 400(\cos 135° + i \sin 135°)$$
$$= -282.84 + i282.84$$
$$\text{Wind speed} = 10(\cos 170° + i \sin 170°)$$
$$= -9.848 + i1.736$$
$$\text{Resultant} = -292.69 + i284.58.$$

This can be reduced to polar form if desired.

EXERCISES

Solve the following Exercises with the aid of complex numbers.

1. Forces of 10, 15, 20, and 30 pounds act in the same plane on a particle. Their angles with the x-axis are 20°, 40°, 120°, and 245° respectively. Find their resultant. Carry out the work graphically as well as arithmetically.

2. An ant crawls across the floor of a railroad car at one mile an hour, making an angle of 45° with the line of motion of the car. The car is moving at the rate of ten miles per hour due north. What is the velocity of the ant with reference to the ground?

3. A steamship is headed northeast at 25 miles per hour. A passenger crosses the ship at four miles per hour. What is the passenger's velocity with reference to the sea as fixed?

4. The resultant of two forces is $10(\cos 60° + i \sin 60°)$. One of the forces is $5(\cos 45° + i \sin 45°)$. What is the other?

5. Ten men attempt to move a heavily loaded truck. Four of the men push on the truck in the desired direction of motion with a force of 100 pounds each. Three men pull with a force of 100 pounds each on a rope which makes an angle of 30° with the desired line of motion. Two men pull with a force of 100 pounds each on a rope that makes an angle of 20° with the desired line of motion. One man pulls with a force of 80 pounds on a rope that makes an angle of 10° with the desired line of motion. What is the force tending to move the truck in the desired line of motion? What force tends to move the truck sideways?

9. Complex Numbers in Algebra

One of the chief problems of algebra is the solution of equations. Consider the equation

$$3x - 2 = 0.$$

In the domain of a child whose only numbers are the positive integers, this equation simply does not have a solution. However, man has

invented the fractions and if we permit the fractions in our problem
this equation has a solution, namely $\frac{2}{3}$.

Consider the equation
$$3x + 2 = 0.$$

In the domain of the older child who has a knowledge of positive
fractions, but who has not been introduced to the negative numbers,
this equation has no solution. Man has invented the negative numbers; admitting the positive and negative rational numbers and zero,
every equation of the form,

$$ax + b = 0, \qquad a \neq 0,$$

where a and b are integers, has a solution.

Consider the equation
$$x^2 - 2 = 0.$$

In order to solve this equation it is necessary to invent an irrational
number, $\sqrt{2}$.

Consider the equation
$$x^2 + 2 = 0.$$

In order to solve equations of this type it is necessary to invent the
imaginary complex numbers.

Now the question arises: If we admit the complex numbers, do
all equations have roots or will it be necessary to invent further
numbers? The most important type of equation is the integral
rational equation.

DEFINITION: *An equation of the type*
$$a_0 x^n + a_1 x^{n-1} + \cdots + a_n = 0,$$
where n is a positive integer and $a_0, a_1, \cdots, a_n$ any complex numbers,
$a_0 \neq 0$ is called an integral rational equation.

With this definition in mind we state without proof a most
important theorem.

Fundamental Theorem of Algebra: *Every integral rational equation*
is satisfied by at least one complex number.

It is difficult to overemphasize the importance of this theorem.[1]
It means, roughly speaking, that the many problems which center

[1]A very simple equation which is not integral rational and which has no root is
$$\sqrt{x + 1} + \sqrt{x} = 0$$

around the integral rational equation fall within the scope of the complex number system.

Example 1

$$x^2 = -1$$

Roots are $\pm i$, $[0 \pm 1i]$

Example 2

$$x^2 + x + 1 = 0$$

Roots are $-\frac{1}{2} \pm \sqrt{\frac{3}{2}}i$

Example 3

$$x^2 - 5x + 6 = 0$$

Roots are 2, 3, $[2 + 0i, 3 + 0i]$

Example 4

$$x^7 + 6ix^6 + 5x^4 + 4x^3 + (3i - 1)x^2 + (-6\,i)x + 15 = 0$$

Roots are unknown but we know that there is at least one complex number which satisfies this equation.

EXERCISES

Solve the following equations.

1. $2x^2 - 5x - 1 = 0$ 2. $3x^2 - x + 7 = 0$
3. $x^2 + x + 4 = 0$ 4. $3x^2 + x + 4 = 0$
5. $x^2 + x + 7 = 0$ 6. $2x^2 + 4x - 3 = 0$
7. $x^5 + 32 = 0$ 8. $x^3 = 1$

10. The Quadratic Formula

Given the equation

$$ax^2 + bx + c = 0, \ a \neq 0.$$

Roots of this equation are

$$\frac{-b \pm \sqrt{b^2 - 4ac}}{2a}$$

Here the numbers a, b, c may be imaginary. In case $b^2 - 4ac$ is other than a positive real number or zero, it is necessary to explain the value assigned to $\sqrt{b^2 - 4ac}$. It may be either of two values. We do not have the simple convention of choosing the positive real value as we do when $b^2 - 4ac$ is a positive real number.

Example
$$x^2 + 2ix - i = 0$$
$$x = -1 \pm \sqrt{-1 + i}$$

Let
$$\sqrt{-1 + i} = \sqrt[4]{2}(\cos 72.5° + i \sin 72.5°)$$

Then
$$-\sqrt{-1 + i} = -\sqrt[4]{2}(\cos 72.5° + i \sin 27.5°)$$

EXERCISES

Solve the following quadratic equations.
1. $3ix^2 + 17 - 4i = 0$ 2. $3x^2 + (1 + i)x - 2i = 0$
3. $x^2 - 8ix + (1 + i) = 0$ 4. $(1 + i)x^2 - 7ix + 4 = 0$
5. $ix^2 - ix + 1 = 0$ 6. $(1 + i)^2x^2 - (i - 1)x + (1 + i) = 0$

11. Graph of the Real Quadratic Function

Let a, b, c be real. We have already studied the graph of
$$y = ax^2 + bx + c.$$
This was done when quadratic equations were studied first in the algebra course. The graph is a parable with axis vertical. Thus,

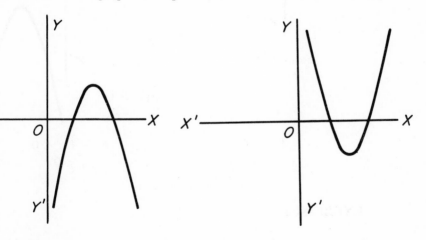

FIGURE 57   FIGURE 58

$$y = ax^2 + bx + c, \; a > 0 \qquad y = ax^2 + bx + c, \; a < 0$$
$$b^2 - 4ac > 0 \qquad\qquad\qquad b^2 - 4ac > 0$$

The abscissas of the points M, N are values which when substituted for x render y zero. They consequently are roots of the equation

$$ax^2 + bx + c = 0.$$

They are real. If the roots are imaginary, the graph cannot reach the axis else there would be real roots. Conversely, if the graph does not reach the axis there can be no real roots and, hence, the roots are imaginary. If the graph just touches the axis but does not cross it, the roots are real and equal.

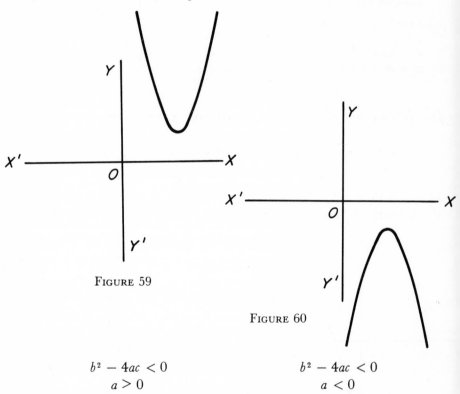

FIGURE 59

FIGURE 60

$$b^2 - 4ac < 0 \qquad\qquad b^2 - 4ac < 0$$
$$a > 0 \qquad\qquad\qquad a < 0$$

EXERCISES

Plot the graphs of the following functions. Tell before making the plot if the graph will cross, just touch, or not touch the x-axis.

1. $x^2 - 5x + 6$ 2. $x^2 + x + 1$
3. $-x^2 + 2x - 1$ 4. $7x^2 - 8x + 2$
5. $3x^2 - 8x - 1$ 6. $\frac{1}{4}x^2 + 2x - 1$

Tables

Certain Constants

$\pi = 3.141\ 592\ 65$ $\qquad \log \pi = 0.497\ 149\ 9$

$\dfrac{\pi}{4} = 0.785\ 398\ 16$ $\qquad \log\dfrac{\pi}{4} = 9.895\ 089\ 9\text{-}10$

$\dfrac{1}{\pi} = 0.318\ 309\ 89$ $\qquad \log\dfrac{1}{\pi} = 9.502\ 850\ 1\text{-}10$

$\sqrt{\pi} = 1.772\ 453\ 85$ $\qquad \log \sqrt{\pi} = 0.248\ 574\ 9$

$\dfrac{1}{\sqrt{\pi}} = 0.564\ 189\ 58$ $\qquad \log \dfrac{1}{\sqrt{\pi}} = 9.751\ 425\ 1\text{-}10$

$e = 2.718\ 281\ 83$ $\qquad \log e = 0.434\ 294\ 5$

1 radian = 57.295 779 5 degrees
= 57° 17′ 44.80625″
1 degree = 0.017 453 292 5 radian

The Greek Alphabet

A	α	Alpha	N	ν	Nu
B	β	Beta	Ξ	ξ	Xi
Γ	γ	Gamma	O	o	Omicron
Δ	δ	Delta	Π	π	Pi
E	ϵ	Epsilon	P	ρ	Rho
Z	ζ	Zeta	Σ	σ	Sigma
H	η	Eta	T	τ	Tau
Θ	θ	Theta	Υ	υ	Upsilon
I	ι	Iota	Φ	ϕ	Phi
K	κ	Kappa	X	χ	Chi
Λ	λ	Lambda	Ψ	ψ	Psi
M	μ	Mu	Ω	ω	Omega

TABLE 1. Trigonometric Functions of Angles

Degrees	sin	csc	tan	cot	sec	cos	
0° 0′	.0000	——	.0000	——	1.000	1.0000	90° 0′
10′	029	343.8	029	343.77	000	000	50′
20′	058	171.9	058	171.89	000	000	40′
30′	087	114.6	087	114.59	000	1.0000	30′
40′	116	85.95	116	85.940	000	0.9999	20′
50′	145	68.76	145	68.750	000	999	10′
1° 0′	.0175	57.30	.0175	57.290	1.000	.9998	89° 0′
10′	204	49.11	204	49.104	000	998	50′
20′	233	42.98	233	42.964	000	997	40′
30′	262	38.20	262	38.188	000	997	30′
40′	291	34.38	291	34.368	000	996	20′
50′	320	31.26	320	31.242	001	995	10′
2° 0′	.0349	28.65	.0349	28.636	1.001	.9994	88° 0′
10′	378	26.45	378	26.432	001	993	50′
20′	407	24.56	407	24.542	001	992	40′
30′	436	22.93	437	22.904	001	990	30′
40′	465	21.49	466	21.470	001	989	20′
50′	494	20.23	495	20.206	001	988	10′
3° 0′	.0523	19.11	.0524	19.081	1.001	.9986	87° 0′
10′	552	18.10	553	18.075	002	985	50′
20′	581	17.20	582	17.169	002	983	40′
30′	601	16.38	612	16.350	002	981	30′
40′	640	15.64	641	15.605	002	980	20′
50′	669	14.96	670	14.924	002	978	10′
4° 0′	.0698	14.34	.0699	14.301	1.002	.9976	86° 0′
10′	727	13.76	729	13.727	003	974	50′
20′	756	13.23	758	13.197	003	971	40′
30′	785	12.75	787	12.706	003	969	30′
40′	814	12.29	816	12.251	003	967	20′
50′	843	11.87	846	11.826	004	964	10′
5° 0′	.0872	11.47	.0875	11.430	1.004	.9962	85° 0′
10′	901	11.10	904	11.059	004	959	50′
20′	929	10.76	934	10.712	004	957	40′
30′	958	10.43	963	10.385	005	954	30′
40′	.0987	10.13	.0992	10.078	005	951	20′
50′	.1016	9.839	.1022	9.7882	005	948	10′
6° 0′	.1045	9.567	.1051	9.5144	1.006	.9945	84° 0′
10′	074	9.309	080	9.2553	006	942	50′
20′	103	9.065	110	9.0098	006	939	40′
30′	132	8.834	139	8.7769	006	936	30′
40′	161	8.614	169	8.5555	007	932	20′
50′	190	8.405	198	8.3450	007	929	10′
7° 0′	.1219	8.206	.1228	8.1443	1.008	.9925	83° 0′
10′	248	8.016	257	7.9530	008	922	50′
20′	276	7.834	287	7.7704	008	918	40′
30′	305	7.661	317	7.5958	009	914	30′
40′	334	7.496	346	7.4287	009	911	20′
50′	363	7.337	376	7.2687	009	907	10′
8° 0′	.1392	7.185	.1405	7.1154	1.010	.9903	82° 0′
10′	421	7.040	435	6.9682	010	899	50′
20′	449	6.900	465	6.8269	011	894	40′
30′	478	6.765	495	6.6912	011	890	30′
40′	507	6.636	524	6.5606	012	886	20′
50′	536	6.512	554	6.4348	012	881	10′
9° 0′	.1564	6.392	.1584	6.3138	1.012	.9877	81° 0′
	cos	sec	cot	tan	csc	sin	Degrees

Table 1 (Continued)

Degrees	sin	csc	tan	cot	sec	cos	
9° 0'	.1564	6.392	.1584	6.3138	1.012	.9877	81° 0'
10'	593	277	614	1970	013	872	50'
20'	622	166	644	6.0844	013	868	40'
30'	650	6.059	673	5.9758	014	863	30'
40'	679	5.955	703	8708	014	858	20'
50'	708	855	733	7694	015	853	10'
10° 0'	.1736	5.759	.1763	5.6713	1.015	.9848	80° 0'
10'	765	665	793	5764	016	843	50'
20'	794	575	823	4845	016	838	40'
30'	822	487	853	3955	017	833	30'
40'	851	403	883	3093	018	827	20'
50'	880	320	914	2257	018	822	10'
11° 0'	.1908	5.241	.1944	5.1446	1.019	.9816	79° 0'
10'	937	164	.1974	5.0658	019	811	50'
20'	965	089	.2004	4.9894	020	805	40'
30'	.1994	5.016	035	9152	020	799	30'
40'	.2022	4.945	065	8430	021	793	20'
50'	051	876	095	7729	022	787	10'
12° 0'	.2079	4.810	.2126	4.7046	1.022	.9781	78° 0'
10'	108	745	156	6382	023	775	50'
20'	136	682	186	5736	024	769	40'
30'	164	620	217	5107	024	9763	30'
40'	193	560	247	4494	025	757	20'
50'	221	502	278	3897	026	750	10'
13° 0'	.2250	4.445	.2309	4.3315	1.026	.9744	77° 0'
10'	278	390	339	2747	027	737	50'
20'	306	336	370	2193	028	730	40'
30'	334	284	401	1653	028	724	30'
40'	363	232	432	1126	029	717	20'
50'	391	182	462	0611	030	710	10'
14° 0'	.2419	4.134	.2493	4.0108	1.031	.9703	76° 0'
10'	447	086	524	3.9617	031	696	50'
20'	476	4.039	555	9136	032	689	40'
30'	504	3.994	586	8667	033	681	30'
40'	532	950	617	8208	034	674	20'
50'	560	906	648	7760	034	667	10'
15° 0'	.2588	3.864	.2679	3.7321	1.035	.9659	75° 0'
10'	616	822	711	6891	036	652	50'
20'	644	782	742	6470	037	644	40'
30'	672	742	773	6059	038	636	30'
40'	700	703	805	5656	039	628	20'
50'	728	665	836	5261	039	621	10'
16° 0'	.2756	3.628	.2867	3.4874	1.040	.9613	74° 0'
10'	784	592	899	4495	041	605	50'
20'	812	556	931	4124	042	596	40'
30'	840	521	962	3759	043	588	30'
40'	868	487	.2994	3402	044	580	20'
50'	896	453	.3026	3052	045	572	10'
17° 0'	.2924	3.420	.3057	3.2709	1.046	.9563	73° 0'
10'	952	388	089	2371	047	555	50'
20'	.2979	357	121	2041	048	546	40'
30'	.3007	326	153	1716	049	537	30'
40'	035	295	185	1397	049	528	20'
50'	062	265	217	1084	050	520	10'
18° 0'	.3090	3.236	.3249	3.0777	1.051	.9511	72° 0'
	cos	sec	cot	tan	csc	sin	Degrees

Table 1 (Continued)

Degrees	sin	csc	tan	cot	sec	cos		
18° 0'	.3090	3.236	.3249	3.0777	1.051	.9511	72°	0'
10'	118	207	281	0475	052	502		50'
20'	145	179	314	3.0178	053	492		40'
30'	173	152	346	2.9887	054	483		30'
40'	201	124	378	9600	056	474		20'
50'	228	098	411	9319	057	465		10'
19° 0'	.3256	3.072	.3443	2.9042	1.058	.9455	71°	0'
10'	283	046	476	8770	059	446		50'
20'	311	3.021	508	8502	060	436		40'
30'	338	2.996	541	8239	061	426		30'
40'	365	971	574	7980	062	417		20'
50'	393	947	607	7725	063	407		10'
20° 0'	.3420	2.924	.3640	2.7475	1.064	.9397	70°	0'
10'	448	901	673	7228	065	387		50'
20'	475	878	706	6985	066	377		40'
30'	502	855	739	6746	068	367		30'
40'	529	833	772	6511	069	356		20'
50'	557	812	805	6279	070	346		10'
21° 0'	.3584	2.790	.3839	2.6051	1.071	.9336	69°	0'
10'	611	769	872	5826	072	325		50'
20'	638	749	906	5605	074	315		40'
30'	665	729	939	5386	075	304		30'
40'	692	709	.3973	5172	076	293		20'
50'	719	689	.4006	4960	077	283		10'
22° 0'	.3746	2.669	.4040	2.4751	1.079	.9272	68°	0'
10'	773	650	074	4545	080	261		50'
20'	800	632	108	4342	081	250		40'
30'	827	613	142	4142	082	239		30'
40'	854	595	176	3945	084	228		20'
50'	881	577	210	3750	085	216		10'
23° 0'	.3907	2.559	.4245	2.3559	1.086	.9205	67°	0'
10'	934	542	279	3369	088	194		50'
20'	961	525	314	3183	089	182		40'
30'	.3987	508	348	2998	090	171		30'
40'	.4014	491	383	2817	092	159		20'
50'	041	475	417	2637	093	147		10'
24° 0'	.4067	2.459	.4452	2.2460	1.095	.9135	66°	0'
10'	094	443	487	2286	096	124		50'
20'	120	427	522	2113	097	112		40'
30'	147	411	557	1943	099	100		30'
40'	173	396	592	1775	100	088		20'
50'	200	381	628	1609	102	075		10'
25° 0'	.4226	2.366	.4663	2.1445	1.103	.9063	65°	0'
10'	253	352	699	1283	105	051		50'
20'	279	337	734	1123	106	038		40'
30'	305	323	770	0965	108	026		30'
40'	331	309	806	0809	109	013		20'
50'	358	295	841	0655	111	.9001		10'
26° 0'	.4384	2.281	.4877	2.0503	1.113	.8988	64°	0'
10'	410	268	913	0353	114	975		50'
20'	436	254	950	0204	116	962		40'
30'	462	241	.4986	2.0057	117	949		30'
40'	488	228	.5022	1.9912	119	936		20'
50'	514	215	059	9768	121	923		10'
27° 0'	.4540	2.203	.5095	1.9626	1.122	.8910	63°	0'
	cos	sec	cot	tan	csc	sin	Degrees	

Table 1 (Continued).

Degrees	sin	csc	tan	cot	sec	cos	
27° 0'	.4540	2.203	.5095	1.9626	1.122	.8910	63° 0'
10'	566	190	132	9486	124	897	50'
20'	592	178	169	9347	126	884	40'
30'	617	166	206	9210	127	870	30'
40'	643	154	243	9074	129	857	20'
50'	669	142	280	8940	131	843	10'
28° 0'	.4695	2.130	.5317	1.8807	1.133	.8829	62° 0'
10'	720	118	354	8676	134	816	50'
20'	746	107	392	8546	136	802	40'
30'	772	096	430	8418	138	788	30'
40'	797	085	467	8291	140	774	20'
50'	823	074	505	8165	142	760	10'
29° 0'	.4848	2.063	.5543	1.8040	1.143	.8746	61° 0'
10'	875	052	581	7917	145	732	50'
20'	899	041	619	7796	147	718	40'
30'	924	031	658	7675	149	704	30'
40'	950	020	696	7556	151	689	20'
50'	.4975	010	735	7437	153	675	10'
30° 0'	.5000	2.000	.5774	1.7321	1.155	.8660	60° 0'
10'	025	1.990	812	7205	157	646	50'
20'	050	980	851	7090	159	631	40'
30'	075	970	890	6977	161	616	30'
40'	100	961	930	6864	163	601	20'
50'	125	951	.5969	6753	165	587	10'
31° 0'	.5150	1.942	.6009	1.6643	1.167	.8572	59° 0'
10'	175	932	048	6534	169	557	50'
20'	200	923	088	6426	171	542	40'
30'	225	914	128	6319	173	526	30'
40'	250	905	168	6212	175	511	20'
50'	275	896	208	6107	177	496	10'
32° 0'	.5299	1.887	.6249	1.6003	1.179	.8480	58° 0'
10'	324	878	289	5900	181	465	50'
20'	348	870	330	5798	184	450	40'
30'	373	861	371	5697	186	434	30'
40'	398	853	412	5597	188	418	20'
50'	422	844	453	5497	190	403	10'
33° 0'	.5446	1.836	.6494	1.5399	1.192	.8387	57° 0'
10'	471	828	536	5301	195	371	50'
20'	495	820	577	5204	197	355	40'
30'	519	812	619	5108	199	339	30'
40'	544	804	661	5013	202	323	20'
50'	568	796	703	4919	204	307	10'
34° 0'	.5592	1.788	.6745	1.4826	1.206	.8290	56° 0'
10'	616	781	787	4733	209	274	50'
20'	640	773	830	4641	211	258	40'
30'	664	766	873	550	213	241	30'
40'	688	758	916	4460	216	225	20'
50'	712	751	.6959	4370	218	208	10'
35° 0'	.5736	1.743	.7002	1.4281	1.221	.8192	55° 0'
10'	760	736	046	4193	223	175	50'
20'	783	729	089	4106	226	158	40'
30'	807	722	133	4019	228	141	30'
40'	831	715	177	3934	231	124	20'
50'	854	708	221	3848	233	107	10'
36° 0'	.5878	1.701	.7265	1.3764	1.236	.8090	54° 0'
	cos	sec	cot	tan	csc	sin	Degrees

Table 1 (Continued).

Degrees	sin	csc	tan	cot	sec	cos	
36° 0'	.5878	1.701	.7265	1.3764	1.236	.8090	54° 0'
10'	901	695	310	3680	239	073	50'
20'	925	688	355	3597	241	056	40'
30'	948	681	400	3514	244	039	30'
40'	972	675	445	3432	247	021	20'
50'	.5995	668	490	3351	249	.8004	10'
37° 0'	.6018	1.662	.7536	1.3270	1.252	.7986	53° 0'
10'	041	655	581	3190	255	969	50'
20'	065	649	627	3111	258	951	40'
30'	088	643	673	3032	260	934	30'
40'	111	636	720	2954	263	916	20'
50'	134	630	766	2876	266	898	10'
38° 0'	.6157	1.624	.7813	1.2799	1.269	.7880	52° 0'
10'	180	618	860	2723	272	862	50'
20'	202	612	907	2647	275	844	40'
30'	225	606	.7954	2572	278	826	30'
40'	248	601	.8002	2497	281	808	20'
50'	271	595	050	2423	284	790	10'
39° 0'	.6293	1.589	.8098	1.2349	1.287	.7771	51° 0'
10'	316	583	146	2276	290	753	50'
20'	338	578	195	2203	293	735	40'
30'	361	572	243	2131	296	716	30'
40'	383	567	292	2059	299	698	20'
50'	406	561	342	1988	302	679	10'
40° 0'	.6428	1.556	.8391	1.1918	1.305	.7660	50° 0'
10'	450	550	441	1847	309	642	50'
20'	472	545	491	1778	312	623	40'
30'	494	540	541	1708	315	604	30'
40'	517	535	591	1640	318	585	20'
50'	539	529	642	1571	322	566	10'
41° 0'	.6561	1.524	.8693	1.1504	1.325	.7547	49° 0'
10'	583	519	744	1436	328	528	50'
20'	604	514	796	1369	332	509	40'
30'	626	509	847	1303	335	490	30'
40'	648	504	899	1237	339	470	20'
50'	670	499	.8952	1171	342	451	10'
42° 0'	.6691	1.494	.9004	1.1106	1.346	.7431	48° 0'
10'	713	490	057	1041	349	412	50'
20'	734	485	110	0977	353	392	40'
30'	756	480	163	0913	356	.373	30'
40'	777	476	217	0850	360	353	20'
50'	799	471	271	0786	364	333	10'
43° 0'	.6820	1.466	.9325	1.0724	1.367	.7314	47° 0'
10'	841	462	380	0661	371	294	50'
20'	862	457	435	0599	375	274	40'
30'	884	453	490	0538	379	254	30'
40'	905	448	545	0477	382	234	20'
50'	926	444	601	0416	386	214	10'
44° 0'	.6947	1.440	.9657	1.0355	1.390	.7193	46° 0'
10'	967	435	713	0295	394	173	50'
20'	.6988	431	770	0235	398	153	40'
30'	.7009	427	827	0176	402	133	30'
40'	030	423	884	0117	406	112	20'
50'	050	418	.9942	0058	410	092	10'
45° 0'	.7071	1.414	1.000	1.0000	1.414	.7071	45° 0'
	cos	sec	cot	tan	csc	sin	Degrees

TABLE 2. Trigonometric Functions of Numbers

n	sin	tan	cot	cos	n	sin	tan	cot	cos
.00	.0000	.0000	———	1.0000	.50	.4794	.5463	1.830	.8776
.01	.0100	.0100	99.997	1.0000	.51	.4882	.5594	1.788	.8727
.02	.0200	.0200	49.993	.9998	.52	.4969	.5726	1.747	.8678
.03	.0300	.0300	33.323	.9996	.53	.5055	.5859	1.707	.8628
.04	.0400	.0400	24.987	.9992	.54	.5141	.5994	1.668	.8577
.05	.0500	.0500	19.983	.9988	.55	.5227	.6131	1.631	.8525
.06	.0600	.0601	16.647	.9982	.56	.5312	.6269	1.595	.8473
.07	.0699	.0701	14.262	.9976	.57	.5396	.6410	1.560	.8419
08	0799	.0802	12.473	.9968	.58	.5480	.6552	1.526	.8365
.09	.0899	.0902	11.081	.9960	.59	.5564	66.96	1.494	.8309
.10	.0998	.1003	9.967	.9950	.60	.5646	.6841	1.462	.8253
.11	.1098	.1104	9.054	.9940	.61	.5729	.6989	1.431	.8196
.12	.1197	.1206	8.293	.9928	.62	.5810	.7139	1.401	.8139
.13	.1296	.1307	7.649	.9916	.63	.5891	.7291	1.372	.8080
.14	.1395	.1409	7.096	.9902	.64	.5972	.7445	1.343	.8021
.15	.1494	.1511	6.617	.9888	.65	.6052	.7602	1.315	.7961
.16	.1593	.1614	6.197	.9872	.66	.6131	.7761	1.288	.7900
.17	.1692	.1717	5.826	.9856	.67	.6210	.7923	1.262	.7838
.18	.1790	.1820	5.495	.9838	.68	.6288	.8087	1.237	.7776
.19	.1889	.1923	5.200	.9820	.69	.6365	.8253	1.212	.7712
.20	.1987	.2027	3.933	.9801	.70	.6442	.8423	1.187	.7648
.21	.2085	.2131	4.692	.9780	.71	.6518	.8595	1.163	.7584
.22	.2182	.2236	4.472	.9759	.72	.6594	.8771	1.140	.7518
.23	.2280	.2341	4.271	.9737	.73	.6669	.8949	1.117	.7452
.24	.2377	.2447	4.086	.9713	.74	.6743	.9131	1.095	.7385
.25	.2474	.2553	3.916	.9689	.75	.6816	.9316	1.073	.7317
.26	.2571	.2660	3.759	.9664	.76	.6889	.9505	1.052	.7248
.27	.2667	.2768	3.613	.9638	.77	.6961	.9697	1.031	.7179
.28	.2764	.2876	3.478	.9611	.78	.7033	.9893	1.011	.7109
.29	.2860	.2984	3.351	.9582	.79	.7104	1.009	.9908	.7038
.30	.2955	.3093	3.233	.9553	.80	.7174	1.030	.9712	.6967
.31	.3051	.3203	3.122	.9523	.81	.7243	1.050	.9520	.6895
.32	.3146	.3314	3.018	.9492	.82	.7311	1.072	.9331	.6822
.33	.3240	.3425	2.920	.9460	.83	.7379	1.093	.9146	.6749
.34	.3335	.3536	2.827	.9428	.84	.7446	1.116	.8964	.6675
.35	.3429	.3650	2.740	.9394	.85	.7513	1.138	.8785	.6600
.36	.3523	.3764	2.657	.9359	.86	.7578	1.162	.8609	.6524
.37	.3616	.3879	2.578	.9323	.87	.7643	1.185	.8437	.6448
.38	.3709	.3994	2.504	.9287	.88	.7707	1.210	.8267	.6372
.39	.3802	.4111	2.433	.9249	.89	.7771	1.235	.8100	.6294
.40	.3894	.4228	2.365	.9211	.90	.7833	1.260	.7936	.6216
.41	.3986	.4346	2.301	.9171	.91	.7895	1.286	.7774	.6137
.42	.4078	.4466	2.239	.9131	.92	.7956	1.313	.7615	.6058
.43	.4169	.4586	2.180	.9090	.93	.8016	1.341	.7458	.5978
.44	.4259	.4708	2.124	.9048	.94	.8076	1.369	.7303	.5898
.45	.4350	.4831	2.070	.9004	.95	.8134	1.398	.7151	.5817
.46	.4439	.4954	2.018	.8961	.96	.8192	1.428	.7001	.5735
.47	.4529	.5080	1.969	.8916	.97	.8249	1.459	.6853	.5653
.48	.4618	.5206	1.921	.8870	.98	.8305	1.491	.6707	.5570
.49	.4706	.5334	1.875	.8823	.99	.8360	1.524	.6563	.5487
.50	.4794	.5463	1.830	.8776	1.00	.8415	1.557	.6421	.5403

Table 2 (Continued).

n	sin	tan	cot	cos	n	sin	tan	cot	cos
1.00	.8415	1.557	6421	.5403	1.30	.9636	3.602	.2776	.2675
1.01	.8468	1.592	.6281	.5319	1.31	.9662	3.747	.2669	.2579
1.02	.8521	1.628	.6142	.5234	1.32	.9687	3.903	.2562	.2482
1.03	.8573	1.665	.6005	.5148	1.33	.9711	4.072	.2456	.2385
1.04	.8624	1.704	.5870	.5062	1.34	.9735	4.256	.2350	.2288
1.05	.8674	1.743	.5736	.4976	1.35	.9757	4.455	.2245	.2190
1.06	.8724	1.784	.5604	.4889	1.36	.9779	4.673	.2140	.2092
1.07	.8772	1.827	.5473	.4801	1.37	.9799	4.913	.2035	.1994
1.08	.8820	1.871	.5344	.4713	1.38	.9819	5.177	.1931	.1896
1.09	.8866	1.917	.5216	.4625	1.39	.9837	5.471	.1828	.1798
1.10	.8912	1.965	.5090	.4536	1.40	.9854	5.798	.1725	.1700
1.11	.8957	2.014	.4964	.4447	1.41	.9871	6.165	.1622	.1601
1.12	.9001	2.066	.4840	.4357	1.42	.9887	6.581	.1519	.1502
1.13	.9044	2.120	.4718	.4267	1.43	.9901	7.055	.1417	.1403
1.14	.9086	2.176	.4596	.4176	1.44	.9915	7.602	.1315	.1304
1.15	.9128	2.234	.4475	.4085	1.45	.9927	8.238	.1214	.1205
1.16	.9168	2.296	.4356	.3993	1.46	.9939	8.989	.1113	.1106
1.17	.9208	2.360	.4237	.3902	1.47	.9949	9.887	.1011	.1006
1.18	.9246	2.427	.4120	.3809	1.48	.9959	10.983	.0910	.0907
1.19	.9284	2.498	.4003	.3717	1.49	.9967	12.350	.0810	0807
1.20	.9320	2.572	.3888	.3624	1.50	.9975	14.101	.0709	.0707
1.21	.9356	2.650	.3773	.3530	1.51	.9982	16.428	.0609	.0608
1.22	.9391	2.733	.3659	.3436	1.52	.9987	19.670	.0508	.0508
1.23	.9425	2.820	.3546	.3342	1.53	.9992	24.498	.0408	.0408
1.24	.9458	2.912	.3434	.3248	1.54	.9995	32.461	.0308	.0308
1.25	.9490	3.010	.3323	.3153	1.55	.9998	48.078	.0208	.0208
1.26	.9521	3.113	.3212	.3058	1.56	.9999	92.620	.0108	.0108
1.27	.9551	2.224	.3102	.2963	1.57	1.0000	1255.8	.0008	.0008
1.28	.9580	3.341	.2993	.2867	1.58	1.0000	—108.65	—.0092	—.0092
1.29	.9608	3.467	.2884	.2771	1.59	.9998	—52.067	—.0192	—.0192
1.30	.9636	3.602	.2776	.2675	1.60	.9996	—34.233	—.0292	—.0292

TABLE 3. Conversion of Radians to Degrees

Deg	Rad	Min	Rad	Sec	Rad
1	0.01745 33	1	0.00029 09	1	0.00000 48
2	0.03490 66	2	0.00058 18	2	0.00000 97
3	0.05235 99	3	0.00087 27	3	0.00001 45
4	0.06981 32	4	0.00116 36	4	0.00001 94
5	0.08726 65	5	0.00145 44	5	0.00002 42
6	0.10471 98	6	0.00174 53	6	0.00002 91
7	0.12217 30	7	0.00203 62	7	0.00003 39
8	0.13962 63	8	0.00232 71	8	0.00003 88
9	0.15707 96	9	0.00261 80	9	0.00004 36
10	0.17453 29	10	0.00290 89	10	0.00004 85
20	0.34906 59	20	0.00581 78	20	0.00009 70
30	0.52359 88	30	0.00872 66	30	0.00014 54
40	0.69813 17	40	0.01163 55	40	0.00019 39
50	0.87266 46	50	0.01454 44	50	0.00024 24
60	1.04719 76	60	0.01745 33	60	0.00029 09
70	1.22173 05				
80	1.39626 34				
90	1.57079 63				

TABLE 4. Logarithms to Base 10 of Trigonometric Functions

Degrees	log sin	log tan	log cot	log cos	
0° 0'	——	——	——	10.0000	90° 0'
10'	7.4637	7.4637	12.5363	.0000	50'
20'	.7648	.7648	.2352	.0000	40'
30'	7.9408	7.9409	12.0591	.0000	30'
40'	8.0658	8.0658	11.9342	.0000	20'
50'	.1627	.1627	.8373	10.0000	10'
1° 0'	8.2419	8.2419	11.7581	9.9999	89° 0'
10'	.3088	.3089	.6911	.9999	50'
20'	.3668	.3669	.6331	.9999	40'
30'	.4179	.4181	.5819	.9999	30'
40'	.4637	.4638	.5362	.9998	20'
50'	.5050	.5053	.4947	.9998	10'
2° 0'	8.5428	8.5431	11.4569	9.9997	88° 0'
10'	.5776	.5779	.4221	.9997	50'
20'	.6097	.6101	.3899	.9996	40'
30'	.6397	.6401	.3599	.9996	30'
40'	.6677	.6682	.3318	.9995	20'
50'	.6940	.6945	.3055	.9995	10'
3° 0'	8.7188	8.7194	11.2806	9.9994	87° 0'
10'	.7423	.7429	.2571	.9993	50'
20'	.7645	.7652	.2348	.9993	40'
30'	.7857	.7865	.2135	.9992	30'
40'	.8059	.8067	.1933	.9991	20'
50'	.8251	.8261	.1739	.9990	10'
4° 0'	8.8436	8.8446	11.1554	9.9989	86° 0'
10'	.8613	.8624	.1376	.9989	50'
20'	.8783	.8795	.1205	.9988	40'
30'	.8946	.8960	.1040	.9987	30'
40'	.9104	.9118	.0882	.9986	20'
50'	.9256	.9272	.0728	.9985	10'
5° 0'	8.9403	8.9420	11.0580	9.9983	85° 0'
10'	.9545	.9563	.0437	.9982	50'
20'	.9682	.9701	.0299	.9981	40'
30'	.9816	.9836	.0164	.9980	30'
40'	8.9945	8.9966	11.0034	.9979	20'
50'	9.0070	9.0093	10.9907	.9977	10'
6° 0'	9.0192	9.0216	10.9784	9.9976	84° 0'
10'	.0311	.0336	.9664	.9975	50'
20'	.0426	.0453	.9547	.9973	40'
30'	.0539	.0567	.9433	.9972	30'
40'	.0648	.0678	.9322	.9971	20'
50'	.0755	.0786	.9214	.9969	10'
7° 0'	9.0859	9.0891	10.9109	9.9968	83° 0'
10'	.0961	.0995	.9005	.9966	50'
20'	.1060	.1096	.8904	.9964	40'
30'	.1157	.1194	.8806	.9963	30'
40'	.1252	.1291	.8709	.9961	20'
50'	.1345	.1385	.8615	.9959	10'
8° 0'	9.1436	9.1478	10.8522	9.9958	82° 0'
10'	.1525	.1569	.8431	.9956	50'
20'	.1612	.1658	.8342	.9954	40'
30'	.1697	.1745	.8255	.9952	30'
40'	.1781	.1831	.8169	.9950	20'
50'	.1863	.1915	.8085	.9948	10'
9° 0'	9.1943	9.1997	10.8003	9.9946	81° 0'
	log cos	log cot	log tan	log sin	Degrees

Subtract 10 from each entry in this table to obtain the proper logarithm of the indicated trigonometric function.

Table 4 (Continued).

Degrees	log sin	log tan	log cot	log cos	
9° 0'	9.1943	9.1997	10.8003	9.9946	81° 0'
10'	.2022	.2078	.7922	.9944	50'
20'	.2100	.2158	.7842	.9942	40'
30'	.2176	.2236	.7764	.9940	30'
40'	.2251	.2313	.7687	.9938	20'
50'	.2324	.2389	.7611	.9936	10'
10° 0'	9.2397	9.2463	10.7537	9.9934	80° 0'
10'	.2468	.2536	.7464	.9931	50'
20'	.2538	.2609	.7391	.9929	40'
30'	.2606	.2680	.7320	.9927	30'
40'	.2674	.2750	.7250	.9924	20'
50'	.2740	.2819	.7181	.9922	10'
11° 0'	9.2806	9.2887	10.7113	9.9919	79° 0'
10'	.2870	.2953	.7047	.9917	50'
20'	.2934	.3020	.6980	.9914	40'
30'	.2997	.3085	.6915	.9912	30'
40'	.3058	.3149	.6851	.9909	20'
50'	.3119	.3212	.6788	.9907	10'
12° 0'	9.3179	9.3275	10.6725	9.9904	78° 0'
10'	.3238	.3336	.6664	.9901	50'
20'	.3296	.3397	.6603	.9899	40'
30'	.3353	.3458	.6542	.9896	30'
40'	.3410	.3517	.6483	.9893	20'
50'	.3466	.3576	.6424	.9890	10'
13° 0'	9.3521	9.3634	10.6366	9.9887	77° 0'
10'	.3575	.3691	.6309	.9884	50'
20'	.3629	.3748	.6252	.9881	40'
30'	.3682	.3804	.6196	.9878	30'
40'	.3734	.3859	.6141	.9875	20'
50'	.3786	.3914	.6086	.9872	10'
14° 0'	9.3837	9.3968	10.6032	9.9869	76° 0'
10'	.3887	.4021	.5979	.9866	50'
20'	.3937	.4074	.5926	.9863	40'
30'	.3986	.4127	.5873	.9859	30'
40'	.4035	.4178	.5822	.9856	20'
50'	.4083	.4230	.5770	.9853	10'
15° 0'	9.4130	9.4281	10.5719	9.9849	75° 0'
10'	.4177	.4331	.5669	.9846	50'
20'	.4223	.4381	.5619	.9843	40'
30'	.4269	.4430	.5570	.9839	30'
40'	.4314	.4479	.5521	.9836	20'
50'	.4359	.4527	.5473	.9832	10'
16° 0'	9.4403	9.4575	10.5425.	9.9828	74° 0'
10'	.4447	.4622	.5378	.9825	50'
20'	.4491	.4669	.5331	.9821	40'
30'	.4533	.4716	.5284	.9817	30'
40'	.4576	.4762	.5238	.9814	20'
50'	.4618	.4808	.5192	.9810	10'
17° 0'	9.4659	9.4853	10.5147	9.9806	73° 0'
10'	.4700	.4898	.5102	.9802	50'
20'	.4741	.4943	.5057	.9798	40'
30'	.4781	.4987	.5013	.9794	30'
40'	.4821	.5031	.4969	.9790	20'
50'	.4861	.5075	.4925	.9786	10'
18° 0'	9.4900	9.5118	10.4882	9.9782	72° 0'
	log cos	log cot	log tan	log sin	Degrees

Subtract 10 from each entry in this table to obtain the proper logarithm of the indicated trigonometric function.

Table 4 (Continued).

Degrees	log sin	log tan	log cot	log cos	
18° 0'	9.4900	9.5118	10.4882	9.9782	72° 0'
10'	.4939	.5161	.4839	.9778	50'
20'	.4977	.5203	.4797	.9774	40'
30'	.5015	.5245	.4755	.9770	30'
40'	.5052	.5287	.4713	.9765	20'
50'	.5090	.5329	.4671	.9761	10'
19° 0'	9.5126	9.5370	10.4630	9.9757	71° 0'
10'	.5163	.5411	.4589	.9752	50'
20'	.5199	.5451	.4549	.9748	40'
30'	.5235	.5491	.4509	.9743	30'
40'	.5270	.5531	.4469	.9739	20'
50'	.5306	.5571	.4429	.9734	10'
20° 0'	9.5341	9.5611	10.4389	9.9730	70° 0'
10'	.5375	.5650	.4350	.9725	50'
20'	.5409	.5689	.4311	.9721	40'
30'	.5443	.5727	.4273	.9716	30'
40'	.5477	.5766	.4234	.9711	20'
50'	.5510	.5804	.4196	.9706	10'
21° 0'	9.5543	9.5842	10.4158	9.9702	69° 0'
10'	.5576	.5879	.4121	.9697	50'
20'	.5609	.5917	.4083	.9692	40'
30'	.5641	.5954	.4046	.9687	30'
40'	.5673	.5991	.4009	.9682	20'
50'	.5704	.6028	.3972	.9677	10'
22° 0'	9.5736	9.6064	10.3936	9.9672	68° 0'
10'	.5767	.6100	.3900	.9667	50'
20'	.5798	.6136	.3864	.9661	40'
30'	.5828	.6172	.3828	.9656	30'
40'	.5859	.6208	.3792	.9651	20'
50'	.5889	.6243	.3757	.9646	10'
23° 0'	9.5919	9.6279	10.3721	9.9640	67° 0'
10'	.5948	.6314	.3686	.9635	50'
20'	.5978	.6348	.3652	.9629	40'
30'	.6007	.6383	.3617	.9624	30'
40'	.6036	.6417	.3583	.9618	20'
50'	.6065	.6452	.3548	.9613	10'
24° 0'	9.6093	9.6486	10.3514	9.9607	66° 0'
10'	.6121	.6520	.3480	.9602	50'
20'	.6149	.6553	.3447	.9596	40'
30'	.6177	.6587	.3413	.9590	30'
40'	.6205	.6620	.3380	.9584	20'
50'	.6232	.6654	.3346	.9579	10'
25° 0'	9.6259	9.6687	10.3313	9.9573	65° 0'
10'	.6286	.6720	.3280	.9567	50'
20'	.6313	.6752	.3248	.9561	40'
30'	.6340	.6785	.3215	.9555	30'
40'	.6366	.6817	.3183	.9549	20'
50'	.6392	.6850	.3150	.9543	10'
26° 0'	9.6418	9.6882	10.3118	9.9537	64° 0'
10'	.6444	.6914	.3086	.9530	50'
20'	.6470	.6946	.3054	.9524	40'
30'	.6495	.6977	.3023	.9518	30'
40'	.6521	.7009	.2991	.9512	20'
50'	.6546	.7040	.2960	.9505	10'
27° 0'	9.6570	9.7072	10.2928	9.9499	63° 0'
	log cos	log cot	log tan	log sin	Degrees

Subtract 10 from each entry in this table to obtain the proper logarithm of the indicated trigonometric function.

Table 4 (Continued).

Degrees	log sin	log tan	log cot	log cos	
27° 0'	9.6570	9.7072	10.2928	9.9499	63° 0'
10'	.6595	.7103	.2897	.9492	50'
20'	.6620	.7134	.2866	.9486	40'
30'	.6644	.7165	.2835	.9479	30'
40'	.6668	.7196	.2804	.9473	20'
50'	.6692	.7226	.2774	.9466	10'
28° 0'	9.6716	9.7257	10.2743	9.9459	62° 0'
10'	.6740	.7287	.2713	.9453	50'
20'	.6763	.7317	.2683	.9446	40'
30'	.6787	.7348	.2652	.9439	30'
40'	.6810	.7378	.2622	.9432	20'
30'	.6833	.7408	.2592	.9425	10'
29° 0'	9.6856	9.7438	10.2562	9.9418	61° 0'
10'	.6878	.7467	.2533	.9411	50'
20'	.6901	.7497	.2503	.9404	40'
30'	.6923	.7526	.2474	.9397	30'
40'	.6946	.7556	.24444	.9390	20'
50'	.6968	.7585	.2415	.9383	10'
30° 0'	9.6990	9.7614	10.2386	9.9375	60° 0'
10'	.7012	.7644	.2356	.9368	50'
20'	.7033	.7673	.2327	.9361	40'
30'	.7055	.7701	.2299	.9353	30'
40'	.7076	.7730	.2270	.9346	20'
50'	.7097	.7759	.2241	.9338	10'
31° 0'	9.7118	9.7788	10.2212	9.9331	59° 0'
10'	.7139	.7816	.2184	.9323	50'
20'	.7160	.7845	.2155	.9315	40'
30'	.7181	.7873	.2127	.9308	30'
40'	.7201	.7902	.2098	.9300	20'
50'	.7222	.7930	.2070	.9292	10'
32° 0'	9.7242	9.7958	10.2042	9.9284	58° 0'
10'	.7262	.7986	.2014	.9276	50'
20'	.7282	.8014	.1986	.9268	40'
30'	.7302	.8042	.1958	.9260	30'
40'	.7322	.8070	.1930	.9252	20'
50'	.7342	.8097	.1903	.9244	10'
33° 0'	9.7361	9.8125	10.1875	9.9236	57° 0'
10'	.7380	.8153	.1847	.9228	50'
20'	.7400	.8180	.1820	.9219	40'
30'	.7419	.8208	.1792	.9211	30'
40'	.7438	.8235	.1765	.9203	20'
50'	.7457	.8263	.1737	.9194	10'
34° 0'	9.7476	9.8290	10.1710	9.9186	56° 0'
10'	.7494	.8317	.1683	.9177	50'
20'	.7513	.8344	.1656	.9169	40'
30'	.7531	.8371	.1629	.9160	30'
40'	.7550	.8398	.1602	.9151	20'
50'	.7568	.8425	.1575	.9142	10'
35° 0'	9.7586	9.8452	10.1548	9.9134	55° 0'
10'	.7604	.8479	.1521	.9125	50'
20'	.7622	.8506	.1494	.9116	40'
30'	.7640	.8533	.1467	.9107	30'
40'	.7657	.8559	.1441	.9098	20'
50'	.7675	.8586	.1414	.9089	10'
36° 0'	9.7692	9.8613	10.1387	9.9080	54° 0'
	log cos	log cot	log tan	log sin	Degrees

Subtract 10 from each entry in this table to obtain the proper logarithm of the indicated trigonometric function.

Table 4 (Continued).

Degrees	log sin	log tan	log cot	log cos		
36° 0'	9.7692	9.8613	10.1387	9.9080	54°	0'
10'	.7710	.8639	.1361	.9070		50'
20'	.7727	.8666	.1334	.9061		40'
30'	.7744	.8692	.1308	.9052		30'
40'	.7761	.8718	.1282	.9042		20'
50'	.7778	.8745	.1255	.9033		10'
37° 0'	9.7795	9.8771	10.1229	9.9023	53°	0'
10'	.7811	.8797	.1203	.9014		50'
20'	.7828	.8824	.1176	.9004		40'
30'	.7844	.8850	.1150	.8995		30'
40'	.7861	.8876	.1124	.8985		20'
50'	.7877	.8902	.1908	.8975		10'
38° 0'	9.7893	9.8928	10.1072	9.8965	52°	0'
10'	.7910	.8954	.1046	.8955		50'
20'	.7926	.8980	.1020	.8945		40'
30'	.7941	.9006	.0994	.8935		30'
40'	.7957	.9032	.0968	.8925		20'
50'	.7973	.9058	.0942	.8915		10'
39° 0'	9.7989	9.9084	10.0916	9.8905	51°	0'
10'	.8004	.9110	.0890	.8895		50'
20'	.8020	.9135	.0865	.8884		40'
30'	.8035	.9161	.0839	.8874		30'
40'	.8050	.9187	.0813	.8864		20'
50'	.8066	.9212	.0788	.8853		10'
40° 0'	9.8081	9.9238	10.0762	9.8843	50°	0'
10'	.8096	.9264	.0736	.8832		50'
20'	.8111	.9289	.0711	.8821		40'
30'	.8125	.9315	.0685	.8810		30'
40'	.8140	.9341	.0659	.8800		20'
50'	.8155	.9366	.0634	.8789		10'
41° 0'	9.8169	9.9392	10.0608	9.8778	49°	0'
10'	.8184	.9417	.0583	.8767		50'
20'	.8198	.9443	.0557	.8756		40'
30'	.8213	.9468	.0532	.8745		30'
40'	.8227	.9494	.0506	.8733		20'
50'	.8241	.9519	.0481	.8722		10'
42° 0'	9.8255	9.9544	10.0456	9.8711	48°	0'
10'	.8269	.9570	.0430	.8699		50'
20'	.8283	.9595	.0405	.8688		40'
30'	.8297	.9621	.0379	.8676		30'
40'	.8311	.9646	.0354	.8665		20'
50'	.8324	.9671	.0329	.8653		10'
43° 0'	9.8338	9.9697	10.0303	9.8641	47°	0'
10'	.8351	.9722	.0278	.8629		50'
20'	.8365	.9747	.0253	.8618		40'
30'	.8378	.9772	.0228	.8606		30'
40'	.8391	.9798	.0202	.8594		20'
50'	.8405	.9823	.0177	.8582		10'
44° 0'	9.8418	9.9848	10.0152	9.8569	46°	0'
10'	.8431	.9874	.0126	.8557		50'
20'	.8444	.9899	.0101	.8545		40'
30'	.8457	.9924	.0076	.8532		30'
40'	.8469	.9949	.0051	.8520		20'
50'	.8482	9.9975	.0025	.8507		10'
45° 0'	9.8495	10.0000	10.0000	9.8495	45°	0'
	log cos	log cot	log tan	log sin	Degrees	

Subtract 10 from each entry in this table to obtain the proper logarithm of the indicated trigonometric function.

TABLE 5. Logarithms to Base 10 of Numbers

n	0	1	2	3	4	5	6	7	8	9
10	0000	0043	0086	0128	0170	0212	0253	0294	0334	0374
11	0414	0453	0492	0531	0569	0607	0645	0682	0719	0755
12	0792	0828	0864	0899	0934	0969	1004	1038	1072	1106
13	1139	1173	1206	1239	1271	1303	1335	1367	1399	1430
14	1461	1492	1523	1553	1584	1614	1644	1673	1703	1732
15	1761	1790	1818	1847	1875	1903	1931	1959	1987	2014
16	2041	2068	2095	2122	2148	2175	2201	2227	2253	2279
17	2304	2330	2355	2380	2405	2430	2455	2480	2504	2529
18	2553	2577	2601	2625	2648	2672	2695	2718	2742	2765
19	2788	2810	2833	2856	2878	2900	2923	2945	2967	2989
20	3010	3032	3054	3075	3096	3118	3139	3160	3181	3201
21	3222	3243	3263	3284	3304	3324	3345	3365	3385	3404
22	3424	3444	3464	3483	3502	3522	3541	3560	3579	3598
23	3617	3636	3655	3674	3692	3711	3729	3747	3766	3784
24	3802	3820	3838	3856	3874	3892	3909	3927	3945	3962
25	3979	3997	4014	4031	4048	4065	4082	4099	4116	4133
26	4150	4166	4183	4200	4216	4232	4249	4265	4281	4298
27	4314	4330	4346	4362	4378	4393	4409	4425	4440	4456
28	4472	4487	4502	4518	4533	4548	4564	4579	4594	4609
29	4624	4639	4654	4669	4683	4698	4713	4728	4742	4757
30	4771	4786	4800	4814	4829	4843	4857	4871	4886	4900
31	4914	4928	4942	4955	4969	4983	4997	5011	5024	5038
32	5051	5065	5079	5092	5105	5119	5132	5145	5159	5172
33	5185	5198	5211	5224	5237	5250	5263	5276	5289	5302
34	5315	5328	5340	5353	5366	5378	5391	5403	5416	5428
35	5441	5453	5465	5478	5490	5502	5514	5527	5539	5551
36	5563	5575	5587	5599	5611	5623	5635	5647	5658	5670
37	5682	5694	5705	5717	5729	5740	5752	5763	5775	5786
38	5798	5809	5821	5832	5843	5855	5866	5877	5888	5899
39	5911	5922	5933	5944	5955	5966	5977	5988	5999	6010
40	6021	6031	6042	6053	6064	6075	6085	6096	6107	6117
41	6128	6138	6149	6160	6170	6180	6191	6201	6212	6222
42	6232	6243	6253	6263	6274	6284	6294	6304	6314	6325
43	6335	6345	6355	6365	6375	6385	6395	6405	6415	6425
44	6435	6444	6454	6464	6474	6484	6493	6503	6513	6522
45	6532	6542	6551	6561	6571	6580	6590	6599	6609	6618
46	6628	6637	6646	6656	6665	6675	6684	6693	6702	6712
47	6721	6730	6739	6749	6758	6767	6776	6785	6794	6803
48	6812	6821	6830	6839	6848	6857	6866	6875	6884	6893
49	6902	6911	6920	6928	6937	6946	6955	6964	6972	6981
50	6990	6998	7007	7016	7024	7033	7042	7050	7059	7067
51	7076	7084	7093	7101	7110	7118	7126	7135	7143	7152
52	7160	7168	7177	7185	7193	7202	7210	7218	7226	7235
53	7243	7251	7259	7267	7275	7284	7292	7300	7308	7316
54	7324	7332	7340	7348	7356	7364	7372	7380	7388	7396
55	7404	7412	7419	7427	7435	7443	7451	7459	7466	7474
56	7482	7490	7497	7505	7513	7520	7528	7536	7543	7551
57	7559	7566	7574	7582	7589	7597	7604	7612	7619	7627
58	7634	7642	7649	7657	7664	7672	7679	7686	7694	7701
59	7709	7716	7723	7731	7738	7745	7752	7760	7767	7774

Table 5 (Continued).

n	0	1	2	3	4	5	6	7	8	9
60	7782	7789	7796	7803	7810	7818	7825	7832	7839	7846
61	7853	7860	7868	7875	7882	7889	7896	7903	7910	7917
62	7924	7931	7938	7945	7952	7959	7966	7973	7980	7987
63	7993	8000	8007	8014	8021	8028	8035	8041	8048	8055
64	8062	8069	8075	8082	8089	8096	8102	8109	8116	8122
65	8129	8136	8142	8149	8156	8162	9169	8176	8182	8189
66	8195	8202	8209	8215	8222	8228	8235	8241	8248	8254
67	8261	8267	8274	8280	8287	8293	8299	8306	8312	8319
68	8325	8331	8338	8344	8351	8357	8363	8370	8376	8382
69	8388	8395	8401	8407	8414	8420	8426	8432	8439	8445
70	8451	8457	8463	8470	8476	8482	8488	8494	8500	8506
71	8513	8519	8525	8531	8537	8543	8549	8555	8561	8567
72	8573	8579	8585	8591	8597	8603	8609	8615	8621	8627
73	8633	8639	8645	8651	8657	8663	8669	8675	8681	8686
74	8692	8698	8704	8710	8716	8722	8727	8733	8739	8745
75	8751	8756	8762	8768	8774	8779	8785	8791	8797	8802
76	8808	8814	8820	8825	8831	8837	8842	8848	8854	8859
77	8865	8871	8876	8882	8887	8893	8899	8904	8910	8915
78	8921	8927	8932	8938	8943	8949	8954	8960	8965	8971
79	8976	8982	8987	8993	8998	9004	9009	9015	9020	9025
80	9031	9036	9042	9047	9053	9058	9063	9069	9074	9079
81	9085	9090	9096	9101	9106	9112	9117	9122	9128	9133
82	9138	9143	9149	9154	9159	9165	9170	9175	9180	9186
83	9191	9196	9201	9206	9212	9217	9222	9227	9232	9238
84	9243	9248	9253	9258	9263	9269	9274	9279	9284	9289
85	9294	9299	9304	9309	9315	9320	9325	9330	9335	9340
86	9345	9350	9355	9360	9365	9370	9375	9380	9385	9390
87	9395	9400	9405	9410	9415	9420	9425	9430	9435	9440
88	9445	9450	9455	9460	9465	9469	9474	9479	9484	9489
89	9494	9499	9504	9509	9513	9518	9523	9528	9533	9538
90	9542	9547	9552	9557	9562	9566	9571	9576	9581	9586
91	9590	9595	9600	9605	9609	9614	9619	9624	9628	9633
92	9638	9643	9647	9652	9657	9661	9666	9671	9675	9680
93	9685	9689	9694	9699	9703	9708	9713	9717	9722	9727
94	9731	9736	9741	9745	9750	9754	9759	9763	9768	9773
95	9777	9782	9786	9791	9795	9800	9805	9809	9814	9818
96	9823	9827	9832	9836	9841	9845	9850	9854	9859	9863
97	9868	9872	9877	9881	9886	9890	9894	9899	9903	9908
98	9912	9917	9921	9926	9930	9934	9939	9943	9948	9952
99	9956	9961	9965	9969	9974	9978	9983	9987	9991	9996

ANSWERS TO ODD-NUMBERED EXERCISES

Chapter 1

Section 5

9. $(4, 5)$.

11. $5.$

13. $3, -3$.

15. $(7, -1)$, $(-3, -1)$, $(-3, -11)$; $(17, -11)$, $(17, -21)$, $(7, -21)$; $(17, -11)$, $(17, -1)$, $(7, -1)$; $(-3, -11)$, $(-3, -21)$, $(7, -21)$.

Chapter 2

Section 4

3. **(a)** $-\dfrac{2}{3}, -\dfrac{3}{2}, -4, \dfrac{2a+2}{2a-3}, \dfrac{2x+2}{2x-3}, -\dfrac{2x+2}{8x+3}$.

   (b) $-1, -1, 5, 8a^3 - 2a - 1, 8x^3 - 2x - 1,$ $\dfrac{-8x^3 - 20x^2 - 4x - 1}{(2x+1)^3}$.

   (c) $\sqrt{2}, \sqrt{5}, \sqrt{10}, \sqrt{4a^2 + 4a + 2}, \sqrt{4x^2 + 4x + 2},$ $\dfrac{\sqrt{4x^2 + 4x + 2}}{|2x+1|}$.

Chapter 3

Section 10

3. $180°, 90°, 45°, 60°, 30°, \dfrac{180°}{\pi}, \dfrac{360°}{\pi}, \dfrac{540°}{\pi}, -\dfrac{450°}{\pi}, -\dfrac{630°}{\pi}, \dfrac{1404°}{\pi}$.

5. $\dfrac{216°}{160}, \dfrac{90°}{160}, \dfrac{450°}{160}, -\dfrac{117°}{160}$.

7. $\dfrac{\pi}{3200}, \dfrac{10\pi}{3200}, \dfrac{8\pi}{3200}, \dfrac{7\pi}{3200}, -\dfrac{4\pi}{3200}, -\dfrac{2\pi}{3200}, \dfrac{-15\pi}{3200}$.

9. $\dfrac{\pi}{4}$ ins.

11. 125 ft., $\dfrac{2175\pi}{180}$ ft., $\dfrac{7642\pi}{3200}$ ft.

13. $\dfrac{6.25\pi}{12}$ dollars.

15. 10 nautical miles.

17. $\dfrac{44\pi}{27}$ yds.

Chapter 4

Section 2

9. $\dfrac{\pi}{4} + n\pi, \dfrac{3}{4}\pi + n\pi.$

15. $1, -1, 0, 0.$

Section 6

1. (a) $-\cot\alpha, -\tan\alpha, -\csc\alpha, \sec\alpha.$
   (b) $-\tan\alpha, -\cot\alpha, -\sec\alpha, \csc\alpha.$
   (c) $\tan\alpha, \cot\alpha, -\sec\alpha, -\csc\alpha.$
   (d) $\sin\alpha, \cos\alpha, \sec\alpha, \csc\alpha.$
   (e) $\tan\alpha, \cot\alpha, -\sec\alpha, -\csc\alpha.$

3. $\frac{1}{2}\sqrt{3}, -\frac{1}{2}\sqrt{3}, -\frac{1}{3}\sqrt{3}.$

Chapter 5

1. $b = 91.91, c = 95.25, B = 74° \, 47'.$
3. $a = 954.0, b = 299.6, A = 72° \, 34'.$
5. $a = 721.6, A = 80° \, 9', B = 9° \, 51'.$
7. 33.5 ft., $73° \, 24'$
9. 43.6 ft.
11. 11.5 ft.
13. 2.7 ft.   **15.** 3430 miles.   **17.** 16.0 miles.

Chapter 7

Section 2

1. (a) $\sqrt{61}.$ (b) $\frac{1}{2}\sqrt{2a^2 + 10b^2 - 8ab}.$
   (c) $(c^4 + d^4 + 5c^2 + 2d^2 + 3c^2d^2 - 4c^3 - 2cd^2 - 6cd + 2d^3)^{\frac{1}{2}}.$

3. $\sqrt{2(1 - \cos(\beta - \alpha)}.$

Section 5

1. $\frac{1}{2}\sqrt{3}, \frac{1}{2}, \sqrt{3}.$

3. $\dfrac{23}{27}, \dfrac{-10\sqrt{2}}{27}.$

5. $\pm\frac{1}{2}, \pm\frac{1}{2}\sqrt{3}, \pm\dfrac{1}{\sqrt{3}}.$

Section 6

3. $\frac{1}{2}[\sin 5x + \sin x].$
5. $\frac{1}{2}[\cos 2x + \cos x].$
7. $2 \cos 4x \sin x.$

Section 7

$\cos\alpha.\ -\cos\alpha,\ \cot\alpha,\ -\sin\alpha,\ -\cos\alpha.$

Chapter 8

Section 4

5. $\dfrac{2\pi}{k}$.

9. $\dfrac{2\pi}{387.53}$.

Chapter 9

Section 1

1. $4,\ \dfrac{2\pi}{5},\ \dfrac{\pi}{2}$.

3. $\frac{1}{2},\ \pi,\ \dfrac{\pi+1}{2}$.

5. (a) $y = -2\sin 1,\ v = 4\cos 1$.
    (b) $y = 2\sin 1,\ v = 4\cos 1$.
    (c) $y = -2\sin\frac{1}{2},\ v = 4\cos\frac{1}{2}$.

9. $y = +\frac{1}{2}\sin\left(10\ \sqrt{62}\ t - \dfrac{\pi}{2}\right)$.

Section 2

1. $\frac{3}{4}\sin 3$.

Section 3

1. $2\sin 3$ ins.

Section 4

1. $10\sin 3.5$.

Section 5

5. (a) $(y-x)v_0^2 + x^2 g = 0$.
    (b) $(y-\sqrt{3}\,x)\,v_0^2 + 2gx^2 = 0$.

    (c) $\left(y - \dfrac{x}{\sqrt{3}}\right)v_0^2 + \dfrac{2gx^2}{3} = 0$.

Chapter 10

Section 3

1. $-\dfrac{3}{1024}$.

Section 4

1. $5\cdot 4^9,\ \frac{5}{3}(4^{10}-1)$.

3. $\dfrac{1}{3^9},\ \dfrac{1}{2}\left[1 - \dfrac{1}{3^9}\right]$.

5. $\dfrac{3}{2^6}, \dfrac{3\cdot 2^{-6}-3}{\sqrt{2}+1}$.

7. $\sqrt{5}\cdot 7^{\frac{7}{2}}, \dfrac{\sqrt{5}}{1-\sqrt{7}}(7^{-1}-7^4)$.

9. $2(\sqrt{3}-1)^9, \dfrac{\sqrt{3}+1-2(\sqrt{3}-1)^{10}}{2-\sqrt{3}}$.

Section 6

1. $\frac{2}{3}$.

3. Divergent.

5. $\dfrac{18}{99}$.

7. 16.

9. $\dfrac{4}{1+\sqrt{2}-\sqrt{3}}$.

11. $672.3+\dfrac{120}{9900}$.

Section 7

1. 0.

3. 0.

5. 0.

Section 8

Set 1

1. Convergent.

Set 2

1. Convergent.   **5.** Convergent.

3. Convergent.   **7.** Divergent.

Section 10

1. $a^6+6a^5b+15a^4b^2+20a^3b^3+15a^2b^4+6ab^5+b^6$.

3. $x^{-7}-7x^{-5}+21x^{-3}-35x^{-1}+35x-21x^3+7x^5-x^7$.

5. $\dfrac{1}{3^5}[1+3\cdot 10+3^2\cdot 45+3^3\cdot 120+3^4\cdot 210+3^5\cdot 252+$

$\qquad 3^6\cdot 210+3^7\cdot 120+3^8\cdot 45+3^9\cdot 10+3^{10}]$.

7. $a^2+2ab+b^2; a^2-2ab+b^2; a^3+3a^2b+3ab^2+b^3;$
$a^3-3a^2b+3ab^2-b^3$.

9. $\dfrac{15\cdot 14\cdot 13\cdot 12\cdot 11\cdot 10}{6!}a^6b^9$.

Section 11

1. 5.385.

3.   1.09.
5.   2.030.
7.   1.093.
9.   0.385.
11. $(638)10^6$
13. $(7.26)10^{-5}$.

Section 12
a.   1.
c.   1.
e.   ∞
g. $\frac{1}{2}$.
i.   2.

Chapter 11

Section 2
1.   **(a)** 0.8776.   **(b)** 0.0998.   **(c)** 0.9950.

Section 5
1.   **(b)**.
3.   **(a)**.

Chapter 12

Section 1
3.   1.6487.
5.   23.14
7.   **(a)** $e^{-\frac{17}{6}}$.   **(b)** $e^{\frac{7}{4}}$.

Section 3
1.   1.
3. x.
5. $e^{\frac{1}{2}}$.
11.   **(a)** $y = e^x$.   **(b)** $y = e^{x^2}$.   **(c)** $y = e^{\frac{2}{3}}$.

   (d) $y = \dfrac{e^2}{1 - e^2}$.   **(e)** $y = \dfrac{e^2 \pm \sqrt{e^4 + 12e^2 - 4}}{2}$.

17.   0.6932.
19.   1.6094.
21.   4.7875.

Section 5
1.   **(a)** 1. **(b)** 0. **(c)** 2. **(d)** 3. **(e)** 6, **(f)** −1. **(g)** −3.
3. $10^{-\frac{13}{12}}$.

Chapter 13

Section 2

1. 3.162.

3. 0.04742.

5. 113100.

Chapter 14

Section 3

1. Principal values: **(a)** $\dfrac{\pi}{6}$. **(b)** $\dfrac{\pi}{3}$. **(c)** $\dfrac{\pi}{4}$. **(d)** $\dfrac{\pi}{4}$. **(e)** 0.07.

(f) 0.11. **(g)** 0.20. **(h)** 0.25. **(i)** 0.26. **(j)** 1.24. **(k)** 0.89.

3. $\frac{1}{4}(\sqrt{6} + \sqrt{2})$, $\frac{1}{4}(\sqrt{2} - \sqrt{6})$.

5. $\frac{1}{6}\sqrt{3} - \frac{1}{3}\sqrt{2}$.

Section 4

3. **(a)** 12.4. **(b)** approx. 123.4. **(c)** approx. 321.5. **(d)** approx. 512.

5. **(a)** $\pm\frac{4}{5}$. **(b)** $\frac{1}{4}$.

7. Principal values: **(a)** $\dfrac{\pi}{3}$. **(b)** $\dfrac{\pi}{4}$. **(c)** 0.71. **(d)** 0.61.

Chapter 15

1. $\sin^{-1}(-\frac{1}{2})$, $\cos^{-1} 0$.

3. $\cot^{-1} \frac{3}{2}$, $\cot^{-1} 1$.

5. $\frac{1}{2} \cos^{-1} 1$, $\frac{1}{2} \cos^{-1}(-\frac{3}{5}) = \frac{1}{2} \sin^{-1} \frac{4}{5}$.

7. $\sin^{-1} 0$, $\cos^{-1}(\pm\frac{1}{2}\sqrt{2})$.

9. $x = \sin^{-1}(-\frac{5}{13}) = \cos^{-1}(-\frac{12}{13})$, $x = \sin^{-1} 1$.

11. $\sqrt[3]{6}$ approximating $\sin x$ by $x - \dfrac{x^3}{3!}$.

13. Approx. $\pm\sqrt{18 - 10\sqrt{3}}$.

15. $-\dfrac{\pi}{4} + \sin^{-1} \dfrac{3\sqrt{2}}{4}$.

Chapter 16

1. $b = 29.5$, $c = 28.2$, $C = 70°$.

3. $A = 95° 44'$ $B = 40° 28'$, $C = 43° 48'$.

5. $a = 19.95$, $c = 18.00$, $C = 64° 9'$.

7. $a = 94.72$, $b = 69.28$, $B = 43° 51'$.

9. $A = 33° 33'$, $B = 62° 11'$, $C = 84° 16'$.

11. 105 ft.

13. 196.5 ft.

17.   7423 ft.; 3344 ft.
19.   885.22 ft.
21.   1054 lbs.
23.   63° 47′.

Chapter 17

1. $B = 87° 38′$.
5. $a = 91.63$. $B = 37° 45′$, $C = 44° 5′$.
7. $A = 36° 21′$, $B = 51° 50′$, $C = 91° 49′$.
9. $c = 238.9$, $A = 77° 29′$, $B = 44° 56′$.
11. $b = 0.09418$, $c = 0.04822$, $B = 117° 58′$.
13.   0.4590 mi.
15.   65° 25′, 57° 5′.
17.   844.5 ft.
19.   86° 54′ East of South; 196 m.p.h.

Chapter 18

Section 2

1. $(5, 8)$.
3. $(2, -7)$.
5. $(13, -26)$.
7. $(-\frac{55}{2}, 25)$.
9. $(\frac{8}{15}, -\frac{2}{5})$.
11. $(\frac{9}{2}, \frac{5}{2})$.
13. $8 - i$.
15. $80 + 20i$.
17. $(\frac{33}{85} - \frac{4}{85}i)$.
19. -1.
21. 1.
23. i.
25. $-117 + 44i$.
27. $[a^8 - 28a^6b^2 + 80a^4b^4 - 28a^2b^6 + b^4] + i[8a^7b - 56a^5b^3 + 56a^3b^5 + 8ab^7]$.
29. $128 + 160i$.
31. $2, -1$.
33. $-1, -1$.

Section 3
1. $\cos (240° + n360°) + i \sin (240° + n360°)$.

3. $\sqrt{2}\,[\cos\,(135° + n360°) + i\,\sin\,(135 + n360°)].$
5. $\cos\,(0° + n360°) + i\,\sin\,(0° + n360°).$
7. $\cos\,(90° + n360°) + i\,\sin\,(90° + n360°).$
9. $5[\cos\,(53°\ 7' + n360°) + i\,\sin\,(53°\ 7' + n360°)].$
11. $10[\cos\,(-53°\ 7' + n360°) + i\,\sin\,(53°\ 7' + n360°)].$

Section 7
1. $z = 2(\cos\,n60° + i\,\sin\,n60°).$
3. $z = 2(\cos\,n45° + i\,\sin\,n45°).$
5. $z = \cos\dfrac{-90 + n360°}{4} + i\,\sin\dfrac{-90 + n360°}{4}.$

7. $z = \cos\dfrac{-90 + n360°}{7} + i\,\sin\dfrac{-90 + n360°}{7}.$

9. $z = 2\left(\cos\dfrac{90 + n360°}{8} + i\,\sin\dfrac{90 + n360°}{8}\right).$

11. $z = \sqrt[10]{13}\left(\cos\dfrac{123°\ 41' + n360°}{5} + i\,\sin\dfrac{123°\ 41' + n360°}{5}\right).$

Section 8
1. $-2.8 + 3.2i.$

3. $\dfrac{\sqrt{2}}{2}(29 + 21i).$

5. $927.4;\ 231.6.$

Section 9
1. $\dfrac{5 \pm \sqrt{33}}{4}$

3. $\dfrac{-1 \pm \sqrt{15i}}{2}$

5. $\dfrac{-1 \pm \sqrt{27i}}{2}$

7. $2\left(\cos\dfrac{n360°}{5} + i\,\sin\dfrac{n360°}{5}\right).$

Section 10
1. $\dfrac{17 \pm \sqrt{241}}{6}i.$

3. Approx. $\pm 4 + 4i.$
5. Approx. $\frac{1}{2} \pm (-1.22 + 1.58i).$

INDEX